II OM II

PRANAYAM

ITS-PHILOSOPHY & PRACTICE

An Illustrated Treatise on Pranayam, Dhyana and Kundalini Awakening

Swami Ramdev

Published by : **DIVYA PRAKASHAN**
Divya Yog Mandir Trust
Kripalu Bagh Ashram, Kankhal
Hardwar – 249408 (Uttaranchal)

E mail : divyayoga@rediffmail.com

Website : www.divyayoga.com

Telephone: +91-1334-244107, 240008, 246737

Fax : +91-1334-244805

First Edition : 5,000 Copies, July 2006

Price : INR 180, USD 5, EURO 4

Printed at : **Sai Security Printers Limited**
152, DLF Industrial Area
Faridabad -121003 (Haryana)
Phone: +91-129-2272277, 2276370
Fax: +91-129-2256239
E mail : sspdel@saiprinters.com

ISBN No. 81-89235-59-1 (English I-E)

Contents

INTRODUCTION TO THE COLOURED PICTURES GIVEN IN THE BEGINNING OF THE BOOK

Uḍḍiyāna-Bandha
(Abdominal Locking)

Picture - 1

Anulom-vilom Prāṇāyām

Picture - 2

Anuloma-viloma Prāṇāyām

Picture - 3

Bhrāmarī Prāṇāyām

Picture - 4

Mūlādhāra Çhakṛa (Pelvic Plexus)

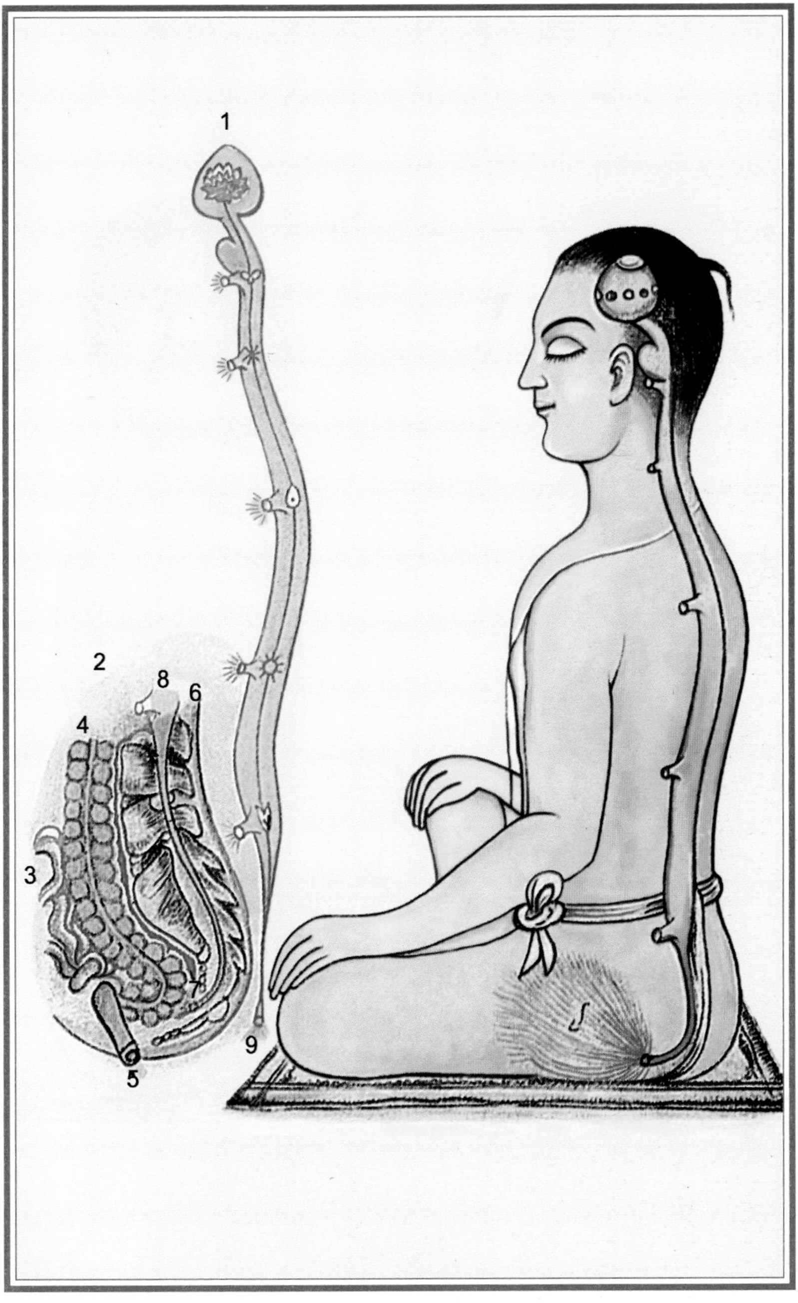

Picture - 5

Svādhiṣṭhāna Çhakṛa (Hypogestric Plexus)

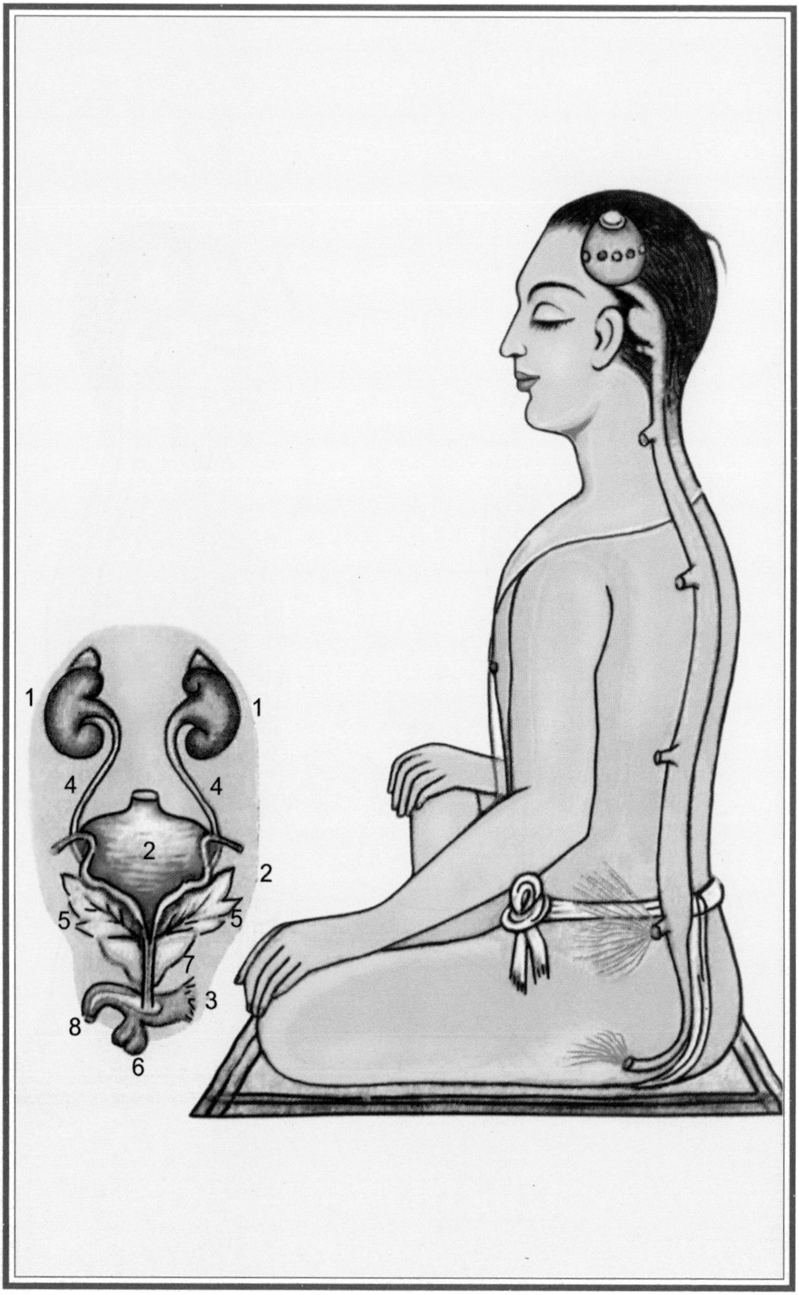

Picture - 6

Maṇipūra Çhakṛa (Solar Plexus)

Picture - 7

Anāhata Çhakṛa
(A magnified view of Cardiac Plexus)

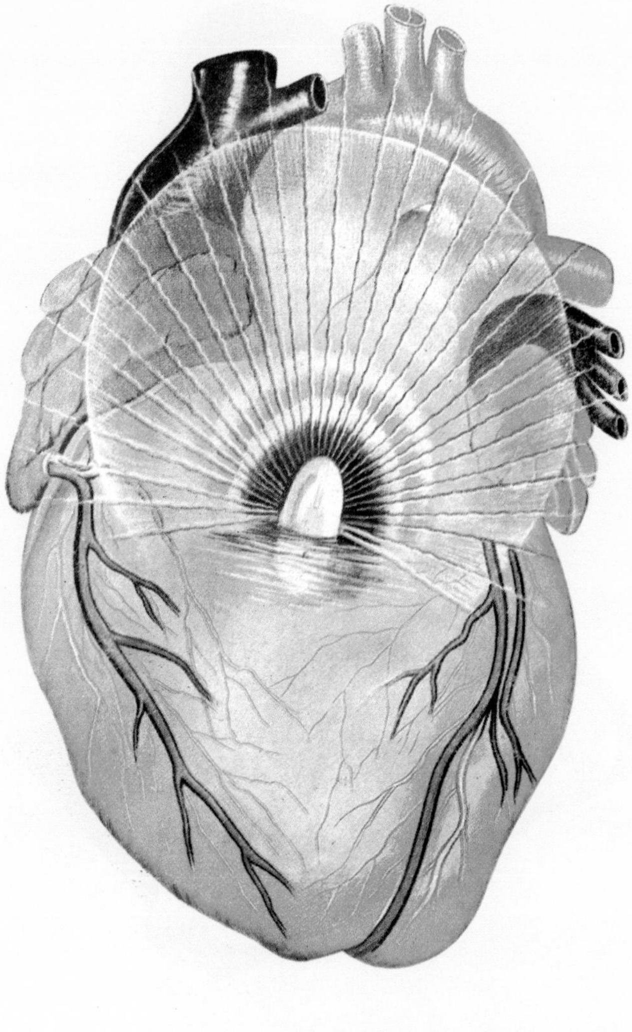

Picture - 8

Hṛdaya Çhakṛa
(Lower Mind Plexus)

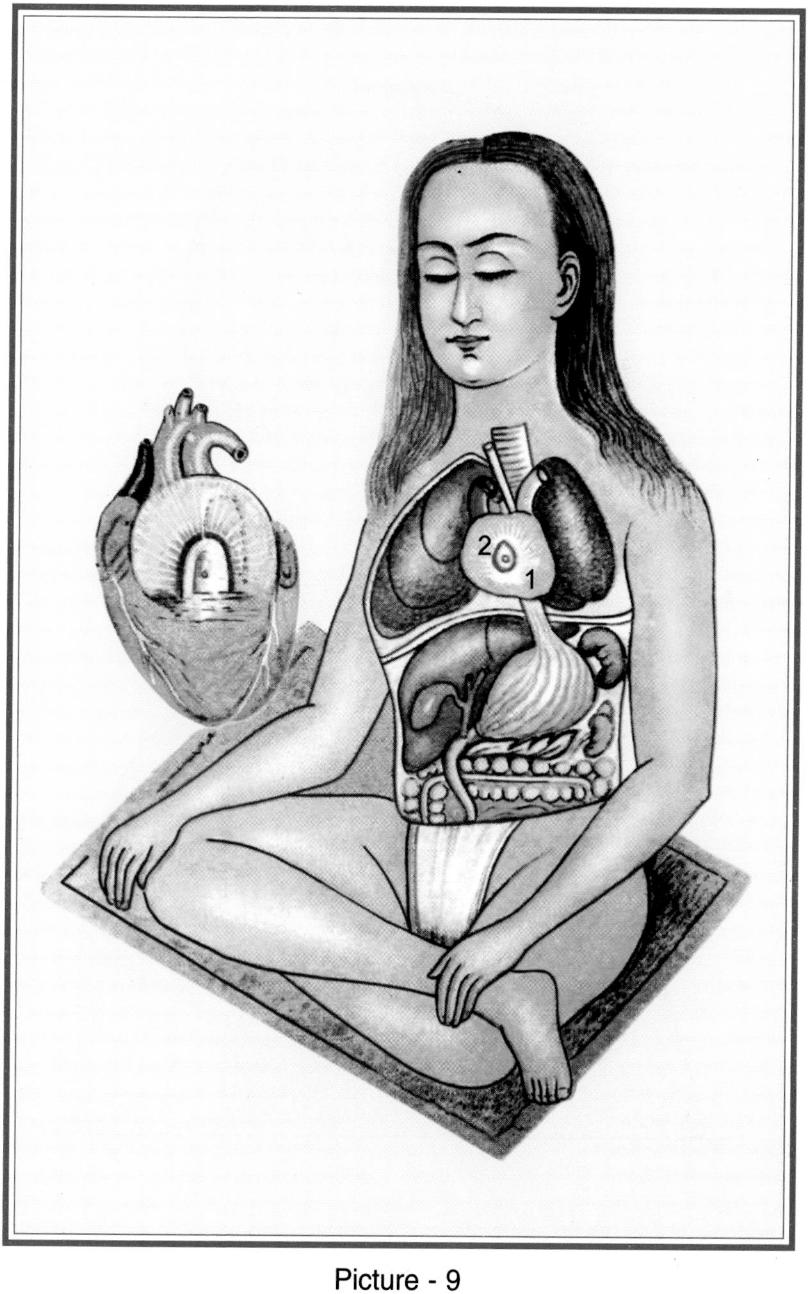

Picture - 9

Viśuddhi Çhaķra (Carotid or Throat Plexus)

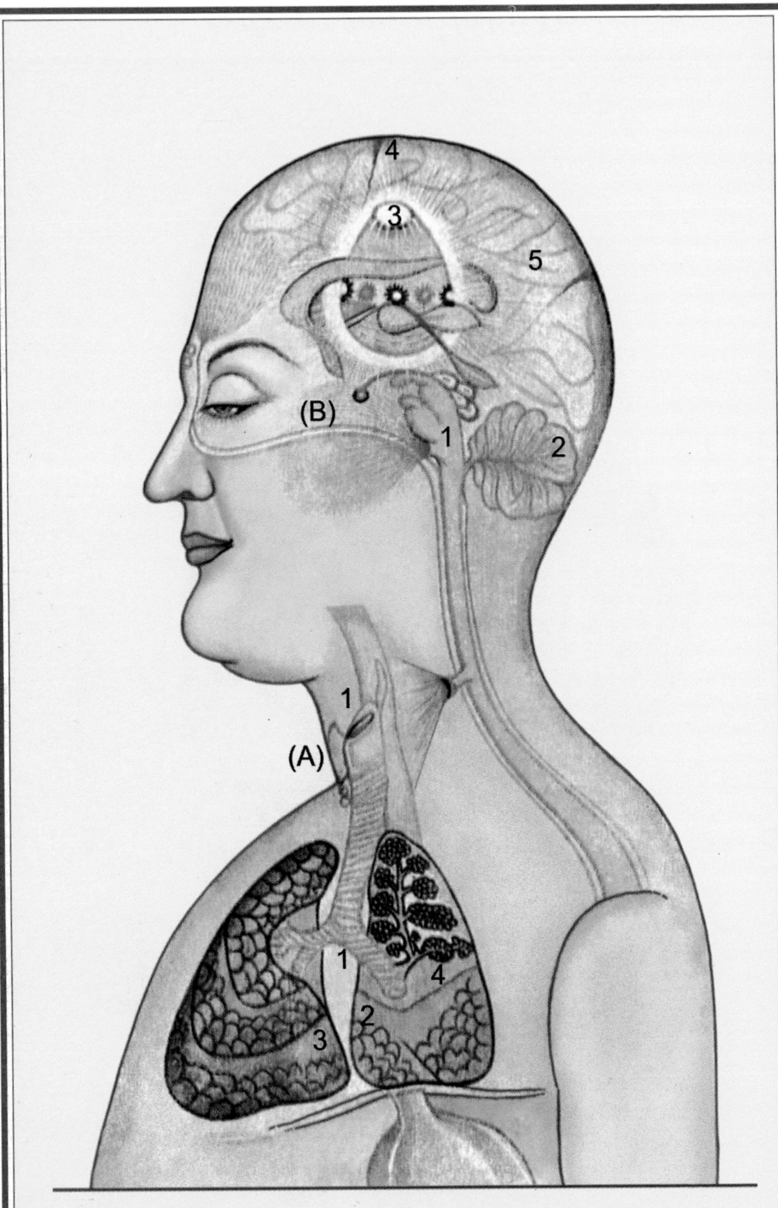

Picture - 10

Suṣhumṇa-Jyoti

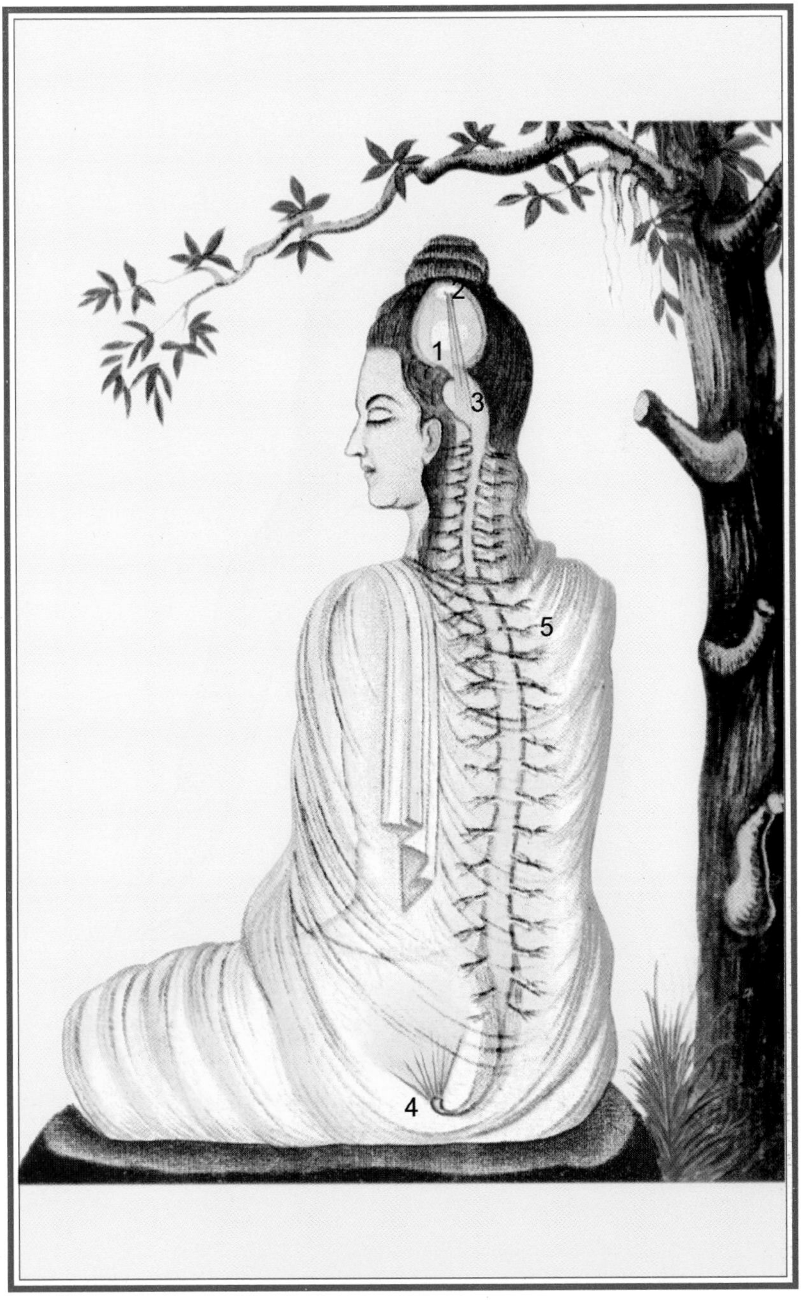

Picture - 11

Çhakṛa Darśana

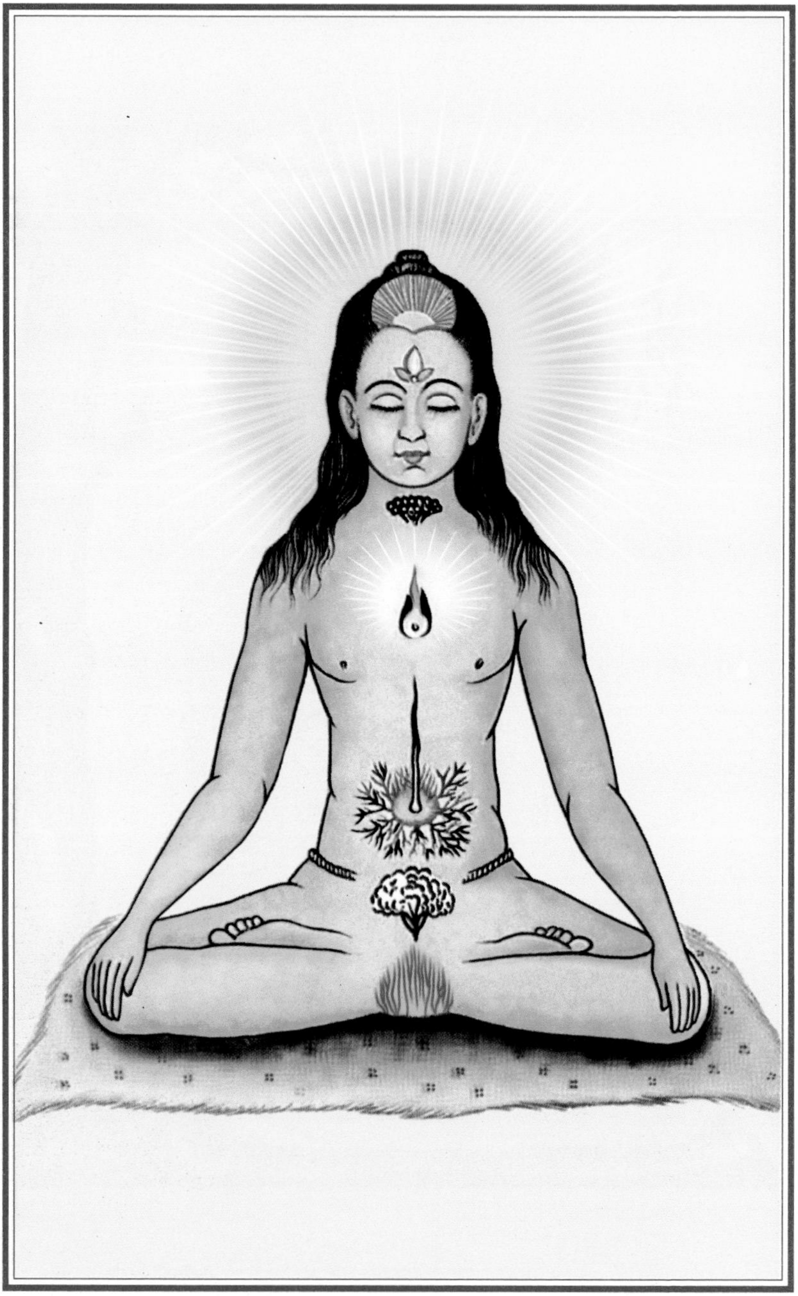

Picture - 12

Divya-dṛiṣṭi

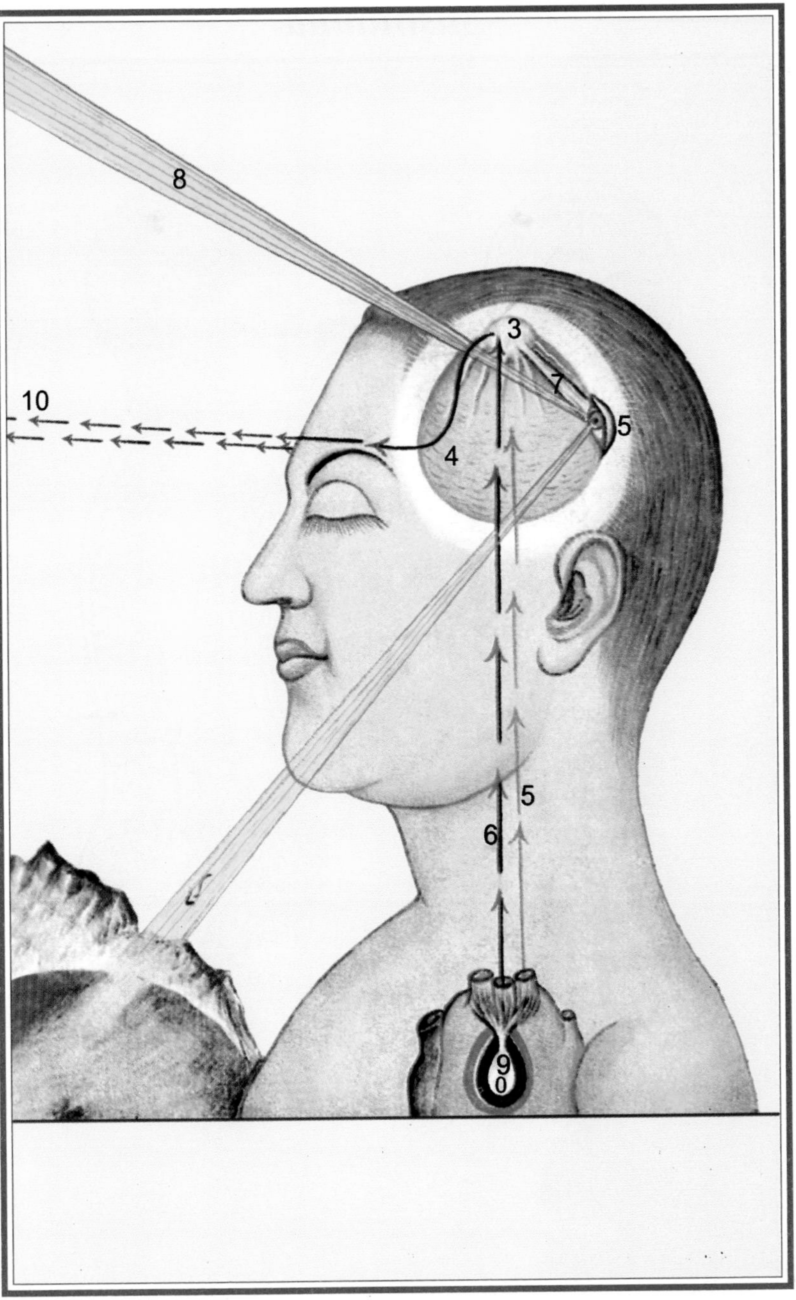

Picture - 13

Piṅgala-Gaṇḍamālā & Organs of Sushumṇa

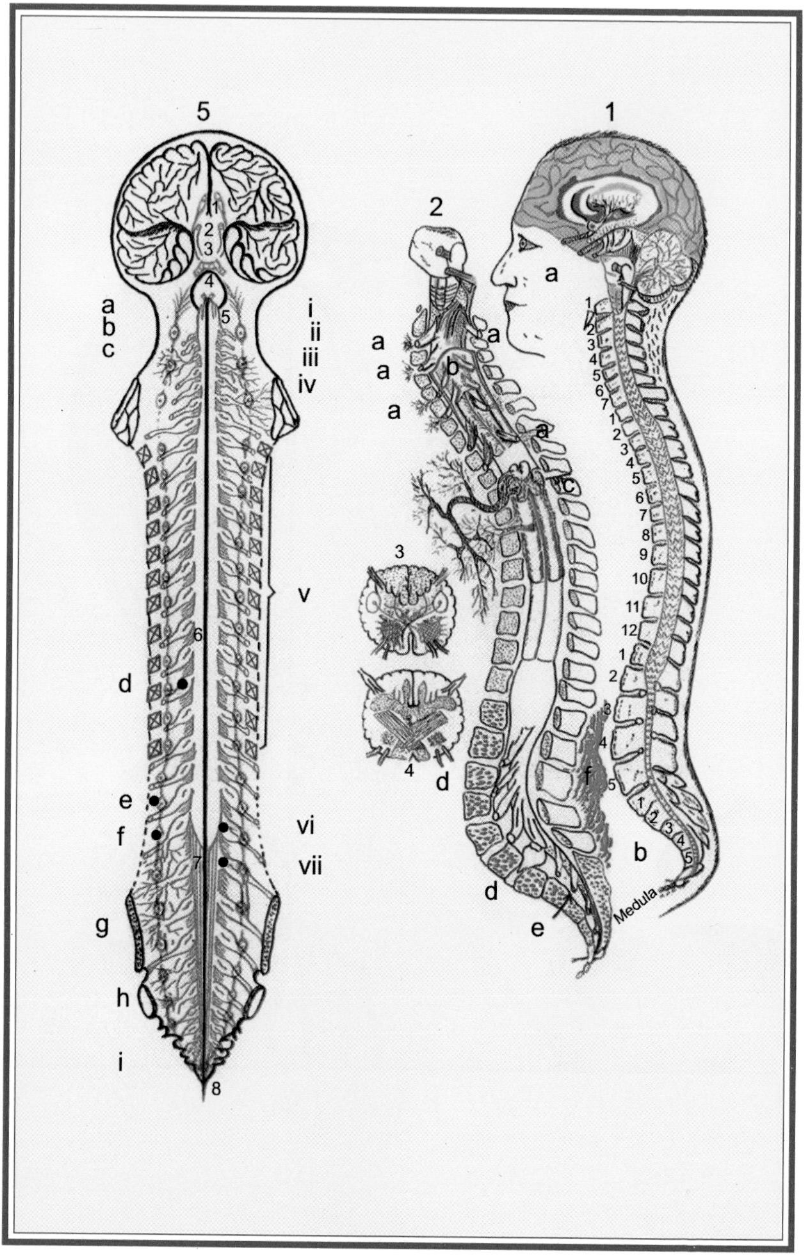

Picture - 14

Gāyatrī Dhyāna

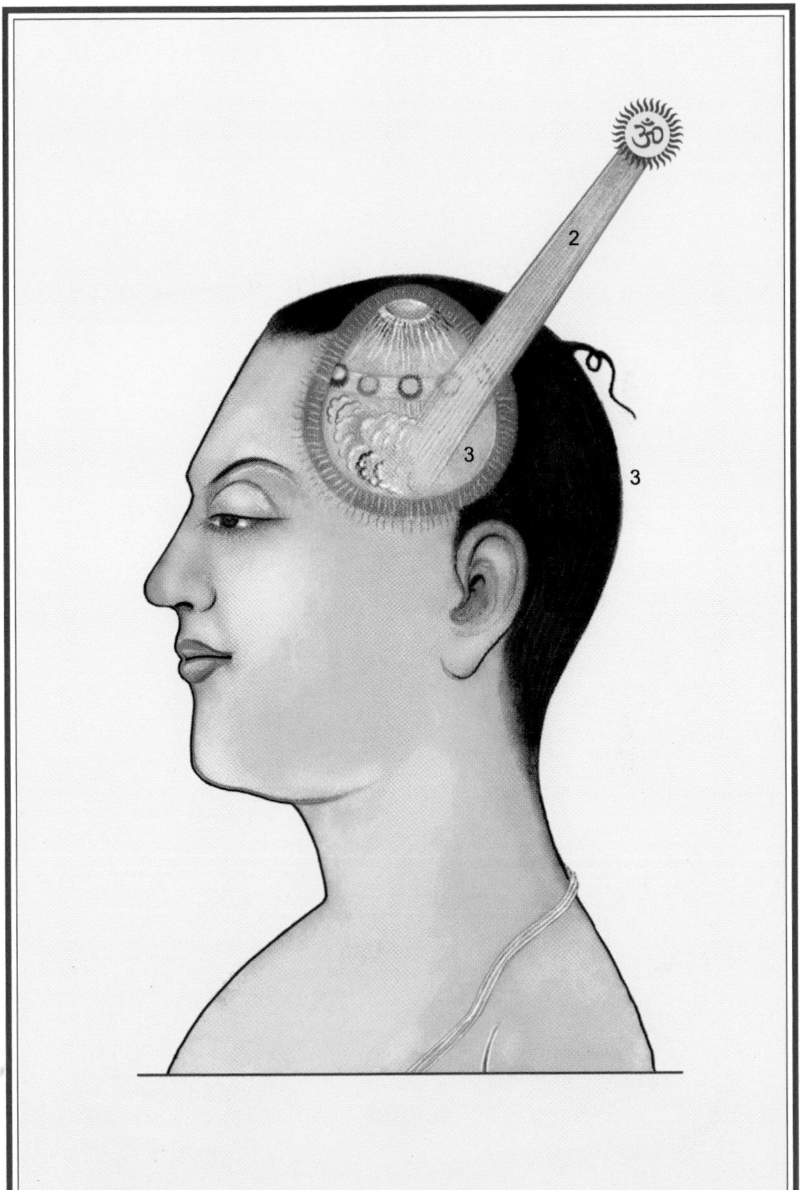

Picture - 15

Divine Vision - Meditation
Vision & Realisation of 'Om Brahma'

Picture - 16

Foreword

"*Dharmārthkāmmo kśhanāmārogyam Mūlmuṭtamam*"-it means that to perform religious rituals, to earn money by various means, to propagate one's family and to seek freedom from the cycle of birth, death and rebirth – to fulfill all of the four desires, one needs to possess good health. Can there be peace and enjoyment when one is sick? Even if one is rich and healthy, leading a lavish life, having all the happiness and pleasures and fame of the materialistic world, then also, if one does not possess good health, his life appears to be a burden on him. If one does not have a healthy mind, does not have a conscious mind, is not physically active and does not have proper blood circulation in the body, is not possessing a strong body and organs therein and his nervous system is weak-that human being will be considered as good as dead. To achieve a healthy body and a healthy mind, there was the advent of *Āyuṛveda* (The system of medicine in which herbs and shrubs are used as medicines for curing diseases). It is still in practice. To get rid of internal filth and flaws and to cleanse the inner self and to achieve the feeling of complete joy by way of interment, sages, saints, divine-ascetics had discovered ascetic processes. '*Prāṇāyām*' (the process of restraining breath) has great importance among these ascetic processes.

For the welfare of the human beings 'Maharshi Patanjali' had devised *Aṣṭāṅg Yog* the eight Yogic practices . It has certain systems, rules and *Āsanas* (Postures & Physical Exercises), to be performed, which help in cleansing and purifying the body and the mind.

Dhaṛna (concentration), *Dhyāna* (meditation) and *Samādhi,* are the exercises that are practised internally in *Yog*. These are the only means and ways of raising one's innerself for attaining utmost pleasure. *Prāṇāyām* acts as a bridge between internal and external Yogic practices. If one wants to keep his body healthy and disease free and wishes to purify his mind and cleanse his soul, then all these are possible with the help of *Prāṇāyām*. By practicing *Prāṇāyām*, the devotee can keep away from the worldly desires, can concentrate and achieve salvation.

Every year several hundred thousands of devotees get rid of physical and mental illnesses, by practically learning the special techniques of ascetics like *Prāṇāyām, Dhyāna*, under the direction of Swami Ramdevji Maharaj, the founder head of Divya Yog Mandir Trust, Kankhal, Hardwar, Uttaranchal (India). Based on his experiences, Swamiji Maharaj is confident that by practicing the process of restraining breath for merely 45 minutes regularly 80% of the diseases like Asthma, Heart diseases, Diabetes, Obesity, Constipation, Acidity etc. can be cured and gradually the person achieves *Samādhi* by the practice of meditation.

We hope that this book will benefit everyone including the children, the aged, the young, the sick, the healthy, householders, persons maintaining celibacy, persons in the third stage of life of a twice born, hermist and general public.

Acharya Balkrishan

Preface

Prāṇāyām is a totally scientific method propounded by divine ascetics and saints and sages like Patanjali, by which incurable diseases can be cured and mental peace and *Samādhi* can also be achieved. Nowadays, some people have forgotten the importance and usage of *Aṣṭāṅg Yog* (the eight Yogic practices) and are just preaching and popularizing *Āsanas* (postures used by ascetics). This is creating doubts about '*Yog*' in the society. For this Maharishi Patanjali's *'Aṣṭāṅg Yog'* is required to be popularized otherwise, eminence of the word '*Yog*' will gradually vanish. In our book named '*Yog – Its Philosophy & Practice*' we have described about '*Yog*' in detail and have left out the subject *Prāṇāyām.* In this book *'Prāṇāyām – Its Philosophy & Practice'*, secrets of *Prāṇāyām* and *Kuṇḍalinī Jāgaran* (the awakening of serpentine power), have been described by giving instances from real life experiences based on experimental experience of lakhs of people. I have a feeling that *Prāṇāyām* is of great importance from the viewpoint of curing of diseases and attaining spiritualism. From the therapeutic point of view, except for the diseases pertaining to bones, enormous benefits and curative effect can be achieved by Yogic exercises by combining *āsanas* and *prāṇāyām*, which are its integral parts. Only *āsanas* are not enough for curing serious and chronic diseases like asthma, heart diseases, nervous disorders, melancholia, diabetes etc. unless, along with the prescribed *Āsanas, Prāṇāyām* is also practiced. *Prāṇāyām*, is so simple and harmless that even children, sick people and the aged can practice it without any harm. This book is being published separately on the request of *Yog* learners. I express my heartfelt gratitude to Shri Laxmichandi Nagar, who is known for his benevolent activities, who has lent to this book a very attractive form and has greatly contributed in making it useful. His incessant help and *guidance* has contributed a great deal in the publication activities of the ashram, which can never be forgotten. I express my gratitude to Acharya Balkrishanji Maharaj who is well versed with *Ayurveda* lore for his *guidance* and advice, I also thank M/s Sai Security Printers Limited, who have published this book and given it a beautiful new look including coloured photographs on the subjects of breath *Prāṇāyām* and *Dhyāna*.

The coloured pictures describing the various *Çhakṛas* (Energy Centres), and their locations in the body, which are included in this book have been taken from the book titled '*Sāṅkhya-Yog aur Brahma-Sākṣātkāra*' written by Yogiraja Shri Jagannath Pathik, from whose spiritual knowledge and experiences, I myself have learnt a lot. At last, I am grateful to the theologian devotee respected Shri Pathikji Maharaj and I am hopeful that this book will be of great help to the learners of '*Yog*'.

Swami Ramdev

Meaning of *Prāṇa* and its Importance

Vāyu – (Air), is one of the five major elements of which our body is constituted of, which keeps us alive and is one of the *tridośas* (three humors of our body) which is our *Prāṇa* (life in the form of breath).

"Pittaḥ Paṅguḥ Kaphaḥ Paṅguḥ Paṅgavo Mala-dhātavaḥ Vāyunā Yatra Nīyante Tatra Gachanti Meghavat Pavansteṣhu Balwān Vibhāgkaraṇānmataḥ Rajoguṇmayaḥ Sūkṣhamaḥ śīto rūkṣo laghuścalaḥ"

(Śārṅgadhara Saṃhitā 5 – 25/26)

*Pitta (*Bile), *Kapha* (Phlegm), the other constituents of the body and the dross elements are all lame, as on their own, they are not capable of going from one place to another or to affect any function of the body. It is the *Vāyu* that takes them from one place to another as the clouds in the sky are drifted from one place to another by the force of the wind. Therefore, in the above mentioned *Doṣas (*humors in the body), only *Vāyu* has the capability of moving and of making other *Doṣas* move. Besides it is strong enough to analyse and separate the ingredients of various elements in the body including the dross element known as excretions of the body like faecal matter, sweat, phlegm, urine etc. On account of possessing the 'active' quality of *Rajoguṇa* (*Rajo* – Royal or King like – it is the quality of being dynamic), it can enter into the tiniest pores of the body, besides being dry, light in weight and quivering.

In the *Upaniṣads* (the holy books containing discourses on divine knowledge); *Prāṇa* has been compared to and given the status of *Brahma* (the creator and the Supreme being), from whom this entire universe has emerged. *Prāṇa* is present in all the cells of the body. The sense organs of the body, take rest, as if asleep or in slumber. But *Prāṇa* always remains active, it never takes rest. Constant movement is its innate character. So long as the *Prāṅic* – (derived from the word '*Prāṇa*') Energy continues to function, it is till that moment that sentient beings remain alive. In the entire universe, *Prāṇa* is the most potent and useful life giving element. Life is dependent on *Prāṇa*. It is due to *Prāṇa* that the physical body of animals and everything in the universe pulsates with life, and continue their communications and functions uninterrupted, without the slightest pause. We see people remaining alive without food or water for several days. But it is impossible to maintain life without "*Prāṇa*" even for a few moments. It is *Prāṅic* energy, which provides us with vital energy, which is the basis of our life and provides us immunity from various kinds of diseases. *Prāṇa* provides energy to all the limbs, organs and important glands of the body including heart, lungs, brain and spinal cord. It is the *Prāṅic* energy, which makes our eyes see, our ears hear, our nose smell and our tongue speak. It is the *Prāṅic* energy again which lends luster to our faces, makes our minds think and enables our alimentary system to digest and assimilate the food that we take. This is what sages say in the *Upaniṣads*:-

"Prāṇo vāva jyeṣṭhaśca śreṣṭhaśca"
"Prāṇsyedaṃ Vaśe sarvaṃ tridivi pratiṣṭhitam"
"Māteva putrān rakṣasva śrīśca prajñāṃ ca vidhehi na Iti"

(Praśnopaniṣad 2/13)

It means "Whatever is there in the universe, within or beyond our cognition, is all in the control of *Prāṇa*. Oh *Prāṇa*! Protect us as a mother protects her sons with affection. Provide us wealth and wisdom.

Types of *Prāṇa*

Prāṇa is a creation of *Brahma*. The inherent quality of *Prāṇa* is "Motion". This quality of *Prāṇa* is felt and experienced in *Vāyu*, which is always in motion, it is due to this property of *Vāyu* we also call it *Prāṇa*. Depending upon its locations and functions in the body, its known by different names like *Prāṇa*, *Apāna* etc. There is only one *Prāṅic* Energy. It is known by different names according to its location and functions. There are mainly five different kinds of *Prāṇas* and five Sub-*Prāṇas* in the body.

Locations and Functions of the five *Prāṇas*:

1. ***Prāṇa*:** It is located in the area between the throat and the heart. It is known by its generic name '*Prāṇa*'.

   Function: It provides energy to the organs of breathing, organs of speech and esophagus and makes them active.

2. ***Apāna*:** It is located in the region between navel (umbilicus) and the tip of the toes. It is called *Apāna*.

   Function: Its function is to cleanse the body of all the dross and used elements like excertions, sweat, phlegm, urine, faces etc. and render the system clean.

3. ***Udāna*:** It is located in the region between the throat and the head. It is called *Udāna*.

   Function: It energises the organs situated in the area above the throat such as the eyes, ears, nostrils and lends luster to the face. It activates the brain alongwith pineal and pituitary glands as well.

4. ***Samāna:*** The *Prāṇa* which activates the region between the heart and the navel is known as *Samāna*.

   Function: It activates and controls the internal functioning of the organs like liver, intestines, spleen, pancreas and all the organs of the digestive system.

5. ***Vyāna:*** This *Prāṇa* is spread over the entire body. It regulates and controls the functioning of all the activities/

processes in the body. It is the *Vyāna Prāṇa* which activates and energises the muscles, the tissues, the joints, *Nāḍīs* - the energy channels and all the organs of the body.

Besides these five *Prāṇas* there are five Sub-*Prāṇas* namely *Devdatta, Nāga, Kṛkala, Kūrma and Dhanañjaya,* which regulates actions like sneezing, winking of the eyes, yawning, scratching on the itching skin, hiccups etc. respectively.

Functioning of all these *Prāṇas* is primarily related to *Prāṇamaya Kośa* - the subtle body and *Prāṇāyām* is mainly responsible for keeping *Prāṇa* and the *Prāṇamaya Kośa* clean, healthy and disease free and due to this reason only *Prāṇāyām* is important and useful. Before beginning the practice of *Prāṇāyām*, it is necessary to have a fair idea of its background. It is for this reason that the initial chapters of the book are devoted to the explanation of different *Prāṇas* and their functions. For easy reference the facts narrated in this chapter are given in the form of a table.

Prāṇa Darśana - Chart

Main *Prāṇa*		Sub *Prāṇa*		*Çhaḳra*	Element
Name	Location	Name	Location		
Prāṇa	In the area around the heart	*Nāga*	A little above the Navel	*Anāhata*	Air (*Vāyu*)
Apāna	Stomach, Anus, Perineum	*Kūrma*	Eye-lids	*Mūladhāra*	Earth (*Prithvi*)
Udāna	In the Heart, Throat, Palate, and the region in between the Eye-Brows and in the Brain	*Devdatta*	Throat and Upper ends of the Trachea	*Viśuddhi*	Ether (*ākāśa*)
Samāna	Navel and the Surrounding expanse	*Kṛkala*	Above the Stomach and the corners of the Trachea	*Maṇipūra*	Fire (*Agni*)
Vyāna	Connected with *Svādhiṣthāna Çhaḳra* and covers the whole body	*Dhanañjaya*	In Bones, Flesh, Skin Blood, Nerves, Hairs etc.	*Svādhiṣthāna*	Water (*Jal*)

Pañchakośas: Five Fold Body (Five Sheaths)

The human soul (the animating force) is surrounded by *Pañcha* (five) Kośas (sheaths), one above the other, and the outer sheaths penetrating the inner ones. These sheaths called *Kośas* are as follows:

1. ***Aṇnamaya Kośa:*** This is the first of the *PañchaKośas* of the body. The *Aṇnamaya Kośa* constitutes the physical body, beginning from its outermost part, the skin, and reaching the inner most recesses, such as bones, flesh, all organs, brain etc. It is related to the element Prithvi (the element Earth), as indicated by its density. Purity of food, proficiency in *Āsanas* and *Prāṇāyām* render it clean and healthy.

2. ***Prāṇamaya Kośa* (*Prāṅic body* or Etheric Body):** It is the second of the *Pañchakośas* of the body. The *Prāṇamaya Kośa* covers and permeates physical, gross body, which we have described above as *Aṇnamaya Kośa*. However, it is not visible unlike the *Aṇnamaya Kośa*; and therefore, most of the people do not know or recognise its existence. The function of the *Prāṇamaya Kośa* is said to be the acquisition of knowledge and to direct the functioning of the physical gross body. *Prāṇa*, which we inhale and exhale, or respirate is divided into ten categories depending upon their location and functions. Of these *Vyāna*, *Udāna*, *Prāṇa*, *Samāna* and *Apāna* are considered to be the main or principal *Prāṇas* and *Dhanañjaya*, *Nāga*, *Kūrma*, *Kṛkala* and *Devadatta* are considered to be the subsidiary *Prāṇas*. The main function of *Prāṇa* is to properly digest the food that we eat, to divide the *Doṣas* in different elements like sweat, faeces and other elements and excrete them from the body. Besides, it also functions as a medium through which we enjoy the pleasures derived from the functioning of the sense organs and the mental processes. By regular practice of *Prāṇāyām*, the *Prāṇamaya Kośa* becomes more energetic and efficient, which in turn energises the *Aṇnamaya Kośa*.

3. ***Manomaya Kośa* (Mental sheath):** This is believed to be the prime body, which activates and guides the functions of the earlier *Kośas* i.e. *Aṇnamaya Kośa* and *Prāṇamaya Kośa*. Mind, Intelligence, Ego and *Çhitta* (Conscience, the source of reasoning, feelings, emotions) are said to be its constituents known collectively as *Antakaraṇa chatuṣṭaya*. It also guides the five sense organs (Eyes, Ears, Nose, Tongue and Skin), which are mostly related to the world outside.

4. ***Vigyanamaya Kośa*:** The fourth body or fourth sheath of the *PañchaKośas* is known as *Vigyanamaya Kośa* that contains within itself, the elements of intelligence and ego. It is responsible for the sense of 'doer', enjoyer etc. It controls the functioning of the sense organs so far as they give rise to the feelings of pain, pleasure and emotions like love, hatred etc. The man who appropriately understands the functioning of this *Kośa* or body, and modulates his thoughts and actions accordingly, keeping himself away from illusions, worldly temptations, attachment etc., remains absorbed in *Dhyāna* and *Samādhi* and achieves the highest state of wisdom known in Yogic lore as *Rtambharā prajñā*. (that knowledge and intelligence which is free from falsehood, illusion, unsteadiness, wavering and other negative qualities.)

5. ***Anandamaya Kośa*:** This *Kośa* is also called by the names *Hiraṇyamaya Kośa* , *Hṛdaya guhā*, *Hṛdaya kośa*, *Liṅga śarīra and Kaaran śarīr* etc. It is said to be located in the heart and is closely related with our inner world. Our lives, the existence of our gross body and our relations with the world as such is dependent on it. On soaring to the level of *Nirbīja Samādhi* (Objectless meditation), the *Sādhaka* (practitioner of *Yog*) becomes free from the shackles of physical life and always enjoys a blissful condition.

Practice of Prāṇa

Prāṇa enters the body through the nostrils. Respiration maintains life and is the basis of *Prāṇāyām*. It is with the support of respiration that the mind peers into the inner world and enables the *Sādhaka* to experience divinity. It is with this objective that the sages of the ancient times formulated different methods of *Prāṇāyām*.

According to *Yog-Darśana* –

"Tasmin sati śvāsapraśvāsayorgatirvicchedaḥ prāṇāyāmah"

(*Yog-Darśana* 2/49)

It means that when you sit in any one of the convenient *āsana* and regulate the act of respiration, it is *Prāṇāyām*. The act of inhaling air into the body so as to reach the lungs, is called inspiration and the act of throwing this air out of the body, is called expiration. There are various stages in *Prāṇāyām* i.e. to inhale air, i.e. *Pūraka*, *Kuṃbhak* - to retain the air so inhaled into the body for some time, *Rēchak* - to exhale the air i.e. to throw the air out of the body and *Bahrya Kuṃbhak* - to keep the air out i.e. not to inhale or allow the air to get into the body. By regular practice, this four step-exercise of *Prāṇāyām* becomes easy to perform. Then, according to

"Tataḥ kṣīyate prakāśāvaraṇam"

(*Yog-Darśana* 2/52)

on acquiring proficiency in these four stages of *Prāṇāyām*, *Çhitta* becomes free from ignorance, the mind is covered by a radiant light of knowledge of the ultimate reality. Then according to

"Dhāraṇāsu ca yogyatā manasaḥ"

(*Yog-Darśana* 2/53)

the *Sādhaka* acquires fitness to reach the sixth stage of *Yog*. When we inhale, it is not only the air or oxygen that enters our body, but along with the air a divine energy also enters which keeps the body alive. Doing *Prāṇāyām* does not mean only taking the air into the body (inhaling) and throwing it out (exhaling), but along with the oxygen, we also take into our body the Vital Energy. This vital energy permeates the entire

Universe and what we inhale and exhale is a fragment of it. Mere exhaling or inhaling is not *Prāṇāyām* but it is a link with the supreme power i.e. God or whatsoever name we call it . To properly build a link with the Supreme Power and to maintain it is *Prāṇāyām*.

Importance of *Prāṇāyām* and its Benefits

As we have stated above, the control or regulation of "*Prāṇa*" (Breath) is called *Prāṇāyām*. All the functions of our body are directly or indirectly related to *Prāṇa*. Without *Prāṇa* there would be no life. In Sanskrit language the word *Jīvan* (life) is derived primarily from *'Jeev-Prāṇa dhāraṇe'* i.e. one is alive, when it is animated by *Prāṇa* and the word death is derived from '*Mṛaṭu Prāntyāgye*'. Life means to hold in or to be animated by *Prāṇa* and death means to sever connection with *Prāṇa*. In *Vedic* and *Upaniṣadic* literature, the importance of *Prāṇa* for human life has been extolled in very clear terms. As said in *Athaṛva-Vēda* ***'Prāṇāāpāānuṃ ṃrityōṛmā pāāt ṣwāḥa'*** where it is prayed that life may be protected from death due to both *Prāṇa* and *Apāna*. '*Manu' (* the lawgiver of the Aryans) says:

"Dahyante dhmāyamānānāṃ dhātūnāṃ hi yathā malāḥ
Thatendriyāṇāṃ dahyante doṣāḥ prāṇasya nigrahāt"

(Manu 6.71)

It means that as the fire cleans dross elements contained in the gold when heated in the same manner *Prāṇāyām* clears the body and mind. In '*Haṭh-Yog Pṛadēpika'* it is said that –

"Prāṇāyāmaireva sarve praśuṣyanti malā iti
Ācāryāṇāu keṣāñcidanyat karma na sammatam"

(Haṭh-Yog Pra. 2.38)

According to '*Gorakśatak'*, through *āsanas, yogīs* should free themselves from *Rajoguṇa*. Bodily and mental abnormalities if any, also may be got rid off by *Prāṇāyām.*

"Āsanena rujo hanti prāṇāyāmena pātakam
Vikāraṃ mānasaṃ yogī pratyāhāreṇa sarvadā"

This shows that *Prāṇa* and mind are closely related to each other. By controlling breath, mind automatically concentrates.

"Cale vāte calaṃ cittaṃ niścale niścalaṃ bhavet"

(Haṭh-Yog Pra. 2.2)

Prāṇāyām has the capacity of freeing the mind from

untruthfulness, ignorance and all other painful and unpleasant experiences of the body and mind; and when the mind becomes clean it becomes easy for the *Sādhaka* to concentrate on the desired object and it becomes possible for him to progress further in the direction of *Dhyāna* and *Samādhi*.

By *Yogāsanas,* we remove the distortions and disabilities of the physical body and bring it into discipline. However *Prāṇāyām* influences the subtle and the physical bodies in a greater measure than *Yogāsanas* do and that too in a perceptible manner. In the human body, lungs, heart and brain hold very important positions and they depend on each other immensely for their health.

Physically, *Prāṇāyām* appears to be a systematic exercise of respiration, which makes the lungs stronger, improves blood circulation, makes the man healthier and bestows upon him the boon of a long life. Physiology teaches us that the air (*Prāṇa*) we breathe in fills our lungs, spreads into the entire body, providing it with essentials from the body, takes them to the heart and then to the lungs, which throws the useless material like carbon dioxide out of the body through the act of exhalation. If this action of the respiratory system is done regularly and efficiently, the lungs become stronger and blood becomes pure.

However, most of the people do not have the habit of breathing deeply with the result that only one-fourth part of the lungs is used and 75 percent remains idle. Like the honeycomb, lungs are made of about 73 million cells, comparable to a sponge in their making. On normal breathing, to which we all are accustomed, only about 20 million pores in the lungs get oxygen, whereas remaining 53 million pores remain deprived of the benefit, with the result that they get contaminated by several diseases like tuberculosis, respiratory diseases, cough, bronchitis etc.

In this way, the inefficient functioning of the lungs affects the process of blood purification. Heart weakens because of this with a constant possibility of untimely death. It is for this reason that the importance of *Prāṇāyām* has come to be recognised, for a healthy long life. Several diseases can be averted by regular practice of *Prāṇāyām*. Hence, it is obvious that the knowledge of the science of *Prāṇāyām* and its regular practice enables a man to lead a healthy and long life. It is for this reason that in several Hindu religious rites, *Prāṇāyām* is found to have been introduced as an essential element.

Mental disturbances like excitement, anxiety, fear, anger, disappointment, lust for sex (lasciviousness) and other mental perversions can be calmed down by regular practice of *Prāṇāyām*. Besides, *Prāṇāyām* practice improves the functions of the brain cells with the result that memory and the faculty of discrimination and observation improves, making it easy for the *sādhaka* to perform concentration and meditation.

Another benefit of *Prāṇāyām* is that by its regular practice, the habit of deep breathing is developed which results in several health benefits. It is said that the nature determines our life span on the basis of the number of respirations we do. Man gets the next birth in accordance with his *kaṛmas* (deeds) done in the present life.

"Sati mūle tadvipāko jātyāyurbhogāḥ"

(Yog-Darśan 2/13)

Our *kaṛmas* (deeds) result in the formation of certain tendencies, which determine the nature of our next birth either as humans or as animals of various categories. A man, who regularly performs *Prāṇāyām*, is required to take lesser number of breaths and therefore lives longer. The table given below in meant to illustrate this point. It shows that the animals that take lesser number of breaths live longer.

No.	Animal	Number of Respirations per 1 minute	No.	Animal	Number of Respirations per 1 minute
1.	Pigeon	34	8.	Sparrow	30
2.	Duck	22	9.	Monkey	30
3.	Dog	28	10.	Pig	36
4.	Horse	26	11.	Goat	24
5.	Cat	24	12.	Snake	16
6.	Elephant	22	13.	Human being	15
7.	Tortoise	5			

From what is stated here, we can conclude that the life span of each of the animals mentioned in the above table depends on the number of respirations each such animal takes within a certain time span. This is indicative of the speed of respiration. It has been observed that the tortoise whose rate of respiration per minute is about 5 breaths lives for about 400 years, establishing the fact that lesser the speed of respiration per minute, longer the life span. A man who does Yogic exercises, respirates about 8 times and if he does meditation regularly this number can be reduced to 4 per minute. Such a person may live for 400 years.

Some rules for *Prāṇāyām*

- Select a clean and peaceful place for doing *Prāṇāyām*. If possible, choose a place near a clean pond or river.
- As there is a lot of pollution in the cities, some kind of incense can be lit like *Guggulu* and purified butter, to create a clean environment at that place, igniting a lamp with purified butter only, can also serve the purpose.
- Sit either in any of the *āsanas*, viz. *Padmāsana, Sidhdhāsana* or *Vajrāsana*, which ever you find convenient. The sheet or cloth (cotton or wool etc.) on which you sit must be a non-conductor of electricity.
- Breathe only through the nose, because by doing so the air which you take in, is filtered. During daytime when you are not sitting for the performance of *Prāṇāyām* make it a habit to respire only through the nose and not through the mouth. Nasal respiration keeps the temperature of the *Nāḍīs (Vessels) 'Iḍā', 'Piṅgalā' and 'Suṣhumṇā'* even. It also prevents foreign and harmful objects from getting into the lungs.
- Like *'Yog'*, *Prāṇāyām* should also be performed four or five hours after taking food. In the morning *Prāṇāyām* should be done after finishing routine acts like cleansing mouth, emptying of bowels etc. It should also be done before *āsanas.* In the beginning *Prāṇāyām* should be done for five or ten minutes gradually the time may be increased up to about 1/2 or 1 hour. Maintain a specific number of repetitions and do not variate. Maintain a specific rhythm. If it is not possible to clean the bowels by morning, at night take some mild laxative like *terminalia chebula* Indian *Harḍaya* a non habit forming medicinal herb, or any other mild laxative. *Kapāla-bhāti Prāṇāyām*, if done regularly for a few days will help in curing constipation.
- Keep your mind calm and composed. However, *Prāṇāyām* can also calm the disturbed mind and keep one happy.

- Methods of *Prāṇāyām* may be varied according to the seasons and your own physical make up and mental attitude. Keep this in mind and modulate the method accordingly. Some *Prāṇāyām*s increase the body temperature, whereas, some bring it down. Some *Prāṇāyām*s maintain the temperature at the normal level.

- If you feel fatigued in the course of doing *Prāṇāyām*, rest for sometime and then begin deep breathing, which will remove fatigue.

- Pregnant women, hungry persons, persons suffering from fever and those who are lustful having no control on their passions should not do *Prāṇāyām*. If you are sick, keep in mind the instructions to be followed by sick persons while during *Prāṇāyām*.

- For prolonged exercises of *Prāṇāyām*, observance of celibacy is necessary. Besides, food should be simple not containing irritating spices. It should be '*Sāttvik*' – (Plain, simple, non-spicy food). Use of cow's milk, *ghēe* (clarified butter), fruits and green vegetables can be said to be ideal food. Moderation also is a good rule to observe.

- Do not strain yourself while doing '*Kuṃbhak*' i.e. retaining the breathed air inside or keeping the air out after exhaling (Breathing in is called '*Pūraka*', retaining the breathed air in is called '*Kuṃbhak*' and exhaling the air out is called '*Rēchak*').

- *Prāṇāyām* does not mean just breathing in, keeping the breathed air in and exhaling it. It also means establishing control on the entire breathing process, and maintaining mental equilibrium, and concentration of mind.

- It is beneficial to chant the *manṭra* (a group of words that carry vibrations and energy) *Om* (the first cosmic soundless sound), aloud and repeat the same several times before doing *Prāṇāyām*. Even recital of sacred songs in the praise of Almighty God or recital of some sacred hymns may be beneficial. This will calm your mind and make you fit for *Prāṇāyām*, because a peaceful mind is very essential while doing *Prāṇāyām*. Mental or loud recitation of *Gāyatrī Manṭra* (considered as one of the greatest manṭra, used in meditation and also for chanting) or any other sacred hymn brings spiritual benefits to the *Sādhaka*.

- See that while doing *Prāṇāyām*, none of your organs such as mouth, eyes, nose, etc. feels any strain and it should be done gradually without any undue stress or strain. All the organs of the body should be kept in normal condition. While doing *Prāṇāyām* sit in an erect posture. Keep your spine and neck straight. This is essential for reaping the full benefit of *Prāṇāyām*.

- Practice of *Prāṇāyām* should be done slowly without any haste, with confidence and prudence.

"Yathā siṃho gajo vyāghro bhaved vaśaḥ śanaiḥ śanaiḥ
Thataiva vaśyate vāyuḥ anyathā hanti sādhakam"

It is said that to tame wild animals like lions, tigers, elephants etc. utmost caution and patience is needed. Any haste in handling them may cause harm to the trainer as a result of their counter attack. Similarly, *Prāṇāyām* should also be done gradually and not in haste.

- If possible *Prāṇāyām* should be done after your usual morning activities like cleansing of mouth, clearing of bowels, bathing etc. However, if it becomes necessary for you to take a bath after *Prāṇāyām*, keep an interval of about 15 to 20 minutes between *Prāṇāyām* and bathing. For acquiring proficiency in *Prāṇāyām* do not depend on books or what is done and preached by others. Seek the guidance of an expert and do *Prāṇāyām* under his direct supervision.

- If you want to get the full advantage of *Prāṇāyām* memorise the following verse from the holy *Bhagvaḍgita* and practice accordingly:

"Yuktāhāra-vihārasya yukta-ceṣṭasya karmasu
Yukta-svapnāvabodhasya yogo bhavati duḥkhahā"

It means that a person whose food habits are not proper, whose daily routine for his day to day work etc. are irregular, that person will not get any benefit out of *Yog* also. And he will still be unhappy after doing *Yog*. In other words one should have discipline in his life for a peaceful and healthy living.

Tri-Bandhās (Three Lockings) Useful in *Prāṇāyām*

With the help of Yogic *Āsanas*, *Prāṇāyām* and *Bandhās*, we prevent the vital energy from flowing out of the body and preserve it inside. The *Bandhās* (to prevent or to lock in). detailed hereafter are extremely helpful. *Prāṇāyām* without *Bandhās* is incomplete. Now we shall describe the *bandhās* one after the other.

Jālandhara Bandhā:

Sit straight either in *Padmāsana* or *Siddhāsana* and breathe in. While doing so, keep your palms on your knees. Lower your neck a little in front so that your chin touches the pit in your neck. Concentrate your eyesight between your brows. Your chest will project itself forward. This *bandhā* has the effect of keeping together the nerves of the neck.

Benefits:

- The voice becomes pleasant and charming.
- Due to the constriction of the neck, *Iḍā* and *Piṅgalā Nāḍīs* also close themselves, directing the *Prāṇa* to *Suṣhumṇā*, the seat of *Kuṇḍalinī*.
- All the diseases of the neck and throat are cured. This *bandhā* is highly beneficial in ailments like thyroid, tonsillitis etc.
- It also awakens the *Viśuddhi Çhakra* (Carotid Plexus).

Uḍḍiyāna Bandhā:

The exercise by which the *Prāṇa* awakens and takes upward course to enter into *Suṣhumṇā Nāḍī* is called '*Uḍḍiyāna Bandhā'*. Standup, bend a little in front and keep your palms on your knees. Breathe out and loosen the muscles of your stomach. While applying J*alandhar Bandhā* lift your chest a little upward and try to push the stomach back, so that it touches the spine on your hind. Keep yourself in this position as long as you can. Then breathe in, rest for sometime and repeat. In the beginning do this *bandhā* exercise thrice. Increase the number of this exercise gradually over a period.

This *bandhā* can be done in yogic *āsanas* like *Padmāsana* or *Siddhāsana*. (Look at Picture No.1).

Benefits:

- This *bandhā* if regularly done as prescribed cures the diseases pertaining the stomach and the organs of the digestive system.
- It awakens and activates all the *Prāṇas* and cleanses the *Maṇipūra Çhaḳra*.

Mūla Bandhā :

Sit in yogic *āsanas* of *Padmāsana* or *Siddhāsana.* Breathe in. Retain the air taken in.Raise the perineum part (part of the body between anus and the genital organs) up. While doing so, the part of the stomach region will be stretched up. This *bandhā* can be done with great ease and convenience, by exhaling and keeping the air outside. Experienced *Yogis* can remain in the position of the *bandhā* for several hours. However, practice of this *bandhā* for a long time should be done under the guidance of some experienced teacher in *Yog*.

Benefits:

- *Apāna Vāyu* takes upward course and amalgamates with *Prāṇa Vāyu*. It awakens *Mūlādhāra Çhaḳra* (Pelvic Plexus) and is helpful in *Kuṇḍalinī Jāgaran* (Awakening of the serpentine power).
- It cures constipation, improves digestion, and cures diseases like piles.
- Makes the semen take upward course and hence is very useful in observance of celibacy.

Maha Bandhā :

Sit in any *āsana* like *Padmāsana* and do all the *bandhās* simultaneously. This *bandhā* bestows upon the *Sādhaka* the benefits of all the three *bandhās* discussed above. All the *bandhās* can be performed in the position of keeping the breath out (*Bāḥya Kuṃbhak*).

Benefits :

- *Prāṇa* takes upward course.
- Purifies semen and makes the body strong.
- This *bandhā*, if regularly done, may result in the confluence of all the three *Nāḍīs*, namely, *Iḍā*, *Piṅgalā* and *Suṣhumṇā*.

Āsanas For *Prāṇāyām*

Your spine must be kept straight while doing *Prāṇāyām*. You can sit in any *Āsana*, such as '*Siddhāsana*', '*Padmāsana*', '*Sukhāsana*' or '*Vajrāsana*' etc. However, if for any reason, you are not in a position to sit on the ground, sit on a chair keeping your back and neck straight. See that your spine remains straight while doing *Prāṇāyām*. Some people nowadays are seen performing *Prāṇāyāms* like *Nāḍī Shōdḥana Prāṇāyām* (for purification of tubular organs like arteries veins etc.) while walking or taking a stroll in the morning. This however is a wrong way of doing *Prāṇāyām* which some times may cause harm. *Prāṇāyām* rouses the *Prāṅic* energy and awakens and activates the *Çhakras* (Energy Centres) attached to the spinal cord. Hence, it is essential to sit in an erect position while doing *Prāṇāyām*. Doing *Prāṇāyām* in any of the postures mentioned above helps in improving the concentration of the mind. (*Dhārṇā* and *Dhyāna*)

Seven Kinds of *Prāṇāyām*

Different treatise advocating or dealing with the subject of *Prāṇāyām* describe several methods and each of them has its own importance. However, it is not possible for most people to do all these exercises daily. Hence, with the blessings of our teachers and in view of our experience, we have evolved seven methods of *Prāṇāyām*, which incorporate into themselves, almost all the peculiarities of *Prāṇāyām* rendering them scientific and useful from a spiritual point of view. All these seven types of *Prāṇāyām* can be done, as a routine and in a time bound programme of about 20 minutes. The person who does these exercises daily and regularly can attain following benefits which are briefly described below :

- All the three *Doṣas (Humors)* - *Vāta*, *Pitta* and *Kapha* get adjusted in proper proportion and abnormalities in them are removed.
- Digestive system improves and diseases pertaining to the digestive organs are cured.
- Diseases pertaining to the lungs, heart and brain are also cured.
- Obesity, diabetes, cholesterol, constipation, flatulence, acidity, respiratory troubles, allergy, migraine, high blood pressure, diseases pertaining to kidneys, sexual disorders of males and females etc. are also cured.
- Immunity develops. Resistance against diseases is stepped up.
- Hereditary diseases like diabetes and heart disease can be avoided.
- Falling of hair or its premature greying, appearance of wrinkles on the face or other parts of the body at a young age, diminution of eyesight, forgetfulness, etc. are relieved and the process of aging is retarded.
- Face becomes bright, luminous and calm.

- Energy *Çhakras* are cleansed and enables the *sādhaka* to awaken the *Kuṇḍalinī*.
- Mind becomes stable and tranquil. A sense of contentment and enthusiasm or zeal develops. Conditions like depression are relieved.
- Performance of Yogic exercises like meditation will be easy.
- All the diseases of the physical and etheric bodies will be cured. Freedom from negative and harmful mental conditions like anger, lasciviousness, greed for money, arrogance etc. will be achieved.
- All the physical and mental disorders and abnormalities are cured and toxins are eradicated from the body.
- Freedom from negative thinking is achieved and the mind develops the habit of positive and constructive thinking.

Now, in the following chapters, we shall discuss these seven methods of *Prāṇāyām*.

First Method - *Bhastrikā Prāṇāyām*

Sit in a comfortable *āsana*. Breathe in through both the nostrils forcefully, till the lungs are full and the diaphragm is stretched. Then breathe out forcefully also, but see that the abdominal cavity does not blow up due to the air breathed in. Depending upon the capacity and health of an individual, this *Prāṇāyām* can be done in three variable speeds viz. slow speed, moderate speed and at high speed. Individuals with weak lungs and heart should do this at a slow speed while performing *Rēchak* and *Pūrak.* A healthy individual and one used to doing it, should do it initially at a slow speed and then gradually increase the speed to moderate and then high. This *Prāṇāyām* should be done for 5 to 10 minutes.

Shiva Saṇkalpa (Vow) at the time of performing *Bhastrikā:*

While inhaling in the process of doing *Bhastrikā* make a vow and focus in your mind as if all the divine powers, purity, peace and joy, all that is good in the universe around you is entering inside your body and that you are getting filled with the divine powers. *Prāṇāyām* done with this kind of vow in mind, imparts a special benefit to the individual.

Special Notes :

- Those suffering from high blood pressure or from any heart disease should not do this *Prāṇāyām*.
- While breathing in the abdominal area should not blow up. You have to fill the air in the chest area, i.e. up to diaphragm, so that the part of the chest with its ribs swells.
- In summer season, reduce the number of repititions of this *Prāṇāyām*.

  Incase both the nostrils do not open on account of ailments like severe cough or sinus etc., such persons should first close the right nostril and do respiration (exhalation as well as inhalation) through the left nostril. Then the left nostril should be closed and respiration should be done by the right nostril. This method of alternate breathing should be continued at the desired speed viz. slow, moderate or fast, till both the nostrils open simultaneously. Then at the end *Prāṇāyām* should be completed by doing *Rēchak* and *Pūrak* through both *Iḍā* and *Piṅgalā*.
- One must do this *Prāṇāyām* for the duration of three to five minutes every day.

  While doing this *Prāṇāyām* keep both the eyes closed and mentally chant the *manṭra* "*OM*" throughout the exercise of *Prāṇāyām*.

Benefits:

- Diseases like cold, cough, allergy, asthma, respiratory diseases of all kinds, are cured. Lungs become strong and due to the heart and head getting adequate quantity of pure and fresh air, health is improved.
- Diseases of the throat like thyroid, tonsils and other ailments of throat are cured.
- This *Prāṇāyām* brings about a proper balance of the three *Doṣas* i.e. *Vāta*, *Pitta*, and *Kapha*, and maintains their balance. Blood is purified and the body gets rid of foreign objects and toxins.
- Stabilizes *Prāṇa* and calms the mind. Helps the upward journey of *Prāṇa* from *Mūlādhāra Çhakra* (Base *Çhakra*)

to *Saḥsrār Çhakṛa* (Cerebral Gland) and is helpful in the *Kuṇḍalinī Jāgaran*.

Second method - *Kapāla-bhāti Prāṇāyām*:

'*Kapāla*' means forehead and '*Bhāti*' means light. Hence, *Kapāla-bhāti* refers to that exercise which makes the forehead luminous and lustrous. *Kapāla-bhāti Prāṇāyām* makes its *sādhaka*'s head luminous. This *Prāṇāyām* is a little different from *Bhasrikā Prāṇāyām*. In *Bhastrikā Prāṇāyām, pūrak* and *rēchak* are done with the same amount of force, where as in *Kapāla-bhāti* more attention is to be given to the act of forceful *rēchak.* In *Kapāla-bhāti*, the *pūrak* is to be done with normal, usual force but the *rēchak* has to be done with as much of force as is at your command. In doing so, the abdominal area, also makes inward and outward movements and considerable force is applied to the *Maṇipūra*, *Svādhiṣthāna* and *Mūlādhāra Çhakṛa*. This *Prāṇāyām* should easily be done for five minutes. In short, breathe in normally and breathe out forcefully, so as to influence the organs of the abdominal area. Persons suffering from acute and chronic diseases must practice if for 15 minutes or more as per the capability.

Shiva Saṇkalpa (Vow) at the time of performing *Kapāla-bhāti*:

While doing this *Prāṇāyām,* think that while exhaling you are throwing out all the diseases from your body. Individuals with mental aberrations like anger, greed, ego, attachment etc. should develop a feeling of throwing out all the negative and injurious elements along with the air exhaled. In this way the feeling of getting rid of diseases while exhaling imparts a special benefit to the individual.

Duration:

Do this *Prāṇāyām* in the beginning for a period of three minutes and gradually increase it to five minutes. Initially, if you feel tired in between, take rest for a while and resume. After practice of about two months, you will be able to perform this *Prāṇāyām* for five minutes at a stretch without any fatigue. This is the total duration for which it should be done. In the beginning, you may feel a little pain in the back or abdomen. But this will disappear after some practice. So do not give up. People whose glands secrete lots of bile inside the body are termed as *Pitta Prakriti*. They should not do this *Prāṇāyām* for more than 2 minutes during summer season.

Benefits:

- Face becomes lustrous and attractive.
- Diseases related to *Kapha* like asthma, respiratory troubles, allergies, sinus, etc. are cured.
- Diseases of heart, lungs and brain get cured.
- Obesity, diabetes, flatulence, constipation, acidity and diseases pertaining to kidneys and prostate glands etc. are cured.
- If done regularly for five minutes daily, it relieves constipation, Blood sugar becomes normal and weight in the abdominal region reduces considerably. Blockages in the arteries are also cleared.
- Peace and stability of mind are achieved. No negative thoughts occur. Troubles like depression are cured.
- *Çhakras* are purified and all *Çhakras* from *Mūlādhāra-Çhakra* to *Saḥsrār Çhakra* are filled with pious Cosmic Energy.
- Organs in the abdominal cavity viz. stomach, pancreas, liver, spleen, intestine, prostrate and kidney function more efficiently and develop immunity towards diseases. This is the best exercise; benefits accrued by this cannot be obtained by several other *āsanas*. It strengthens the intestines and improves digestion.

Third Method - *Bāḥya Prāṇāyām* (with *TriBandhā*)

- Sit in *Padmāsana or Siddhāsana* as indicated. Breathe out or expirate as much as possible.
- Do *Mūlabandhā*, *Uḍḍiyānabandhā* and *Jālandhara bandhā* simultaneously keeping the breath out. Remain in this position as long as you can.

- Then when you desire to breathe in, do it slowly and gradually, unlocking all the *bandhās*.
- Begin breathing normally without retaining the breath in. This can be done from 3 to 21 times.

Shiva Saṇkalpa (Vow) at the time of performing *Bāḥya Prāṇāyām:*

As in *Kapāla-bhāti Prāṇāyām* above, while exhaling think that you are throwing out of your body all abnormalities. The stronger this feeling is, quicker you will be relieved of illnesses. These positive thoughts kill the negative thoughts and quickly give good results to the practitioner.

Benefits:

- This *Prāṇāyām* is absolutely harmless. It stops the fluctuations of the mind. It improves digestion. It is beneficial in all kinds of abdominal ailments. It sharpens intelligence, cleanses the entire body, causes the semen to rise up and cures all kinds of abnormalities related to it. *Bāḥya Prāṇāyām* exerts pressure on all the organs of the abdominal cavity and causes mild pain in this area's weak or diseased parts. For improving the health of these organs this *Prāṇāyām* is very effective and it should be done using all the three *bandhās*.

Fourth method - *Anulom-Viloma Prāṇāyām*

Method to close the nostrils:

To be done by closing the nostrils one after another, close the right nostril by the right hand thumb, and likewise close the left nostril by the 2nd and 3rd fingers (*Maḍhyamā* and *Anāmika*) Keep the palm of the hand in front just above the nose. (See picture 2 and 3).

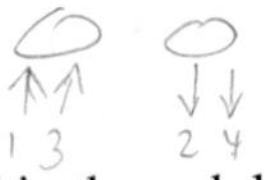

Method:

- *Prāṇa* breathed in through left nostril represents energy of the moon, which symbolizes peace, and has a cooling effect. Hence for purification of *Nāḍīs*, beginning of this *Prāṇāyām* has to be made by the left nostril. Close the right side nostril with the right hand thumb. Inhale slowly through the left nostril till the lungs are filled. Then close the left nostril with the second and third fingers. Open the right nostril and exhale through it. Repeat this exercise slowly in the beginning, and with practice, increase the speed. When you are able to practice this exercise for a long time, inhale with as much force as is possible for you, then exhale also forcefully. This practice of inhalation and exhalation alternatively through the right and left nostril, as indicated above with force, should be done for 3 minutes. If you feel tired, rest for sometimes and resume. Regular practice will enable you to do this *Prāṇāyām* for 10 minutes. After some practice being established, this *Prāṇāyām* should be done for 5 to 10 minutes daily, depending upon one's capacity. However, in summer season it should be done for duration starting from 3 minutes and up to a maximum of 5 minutes. If you practice this *Prāṇāyām* for five minutes regularly on a daily basis, the coiled energy called *Kuṇḍalinī Śhakti* lying in the *Mūlādhāra Çhakṛa* begins to awaken.This is known as *Kuṇḍalinī Jāgaran*. While doing this *Prāṇāyām*, mentally repeat the *manṭra "OM"* so that the mind becomes fit for meditation.

Shiva Saṇkalpa (Vow) at the time of performing *Anulom-Viloma Prāṇāyām:*

While performing this *Prāṇāyām* there develops a feeling in mind that as a result of friction and churning of breath in *Iḍā* and *Piṅgalā Nāḍīs*, there is awakening in *Suṣhumṇā Nāḍī*. A divine light is rising upwards from the eight *Çhakṛas* to the *Saḥsrār Çhakṛa*.

There is a feeling that the whole body is being enlightened by a divine light. As shown in picture no. 16, imagine a divine light on the outside and the inside of the body and try to visualize '*Om Kham Brahm*'. Imagine that the Supreme power is showering divine energy and divine knowledge, that the supreme power is filling you with divine energy. Try to get the initiation of the divine energy by yourself. A *Gurū* (teacher) just inspires you for the divine energy and links the student to divine feelings. Actually the divine energy is showered by the Supreme power himself. *Anulom-Vilom Prāṇāyām* done with these kinds of divine feelings gives better results and benefits individual in all the spheres viz. physically, mentally and spiritually. A divine light will appear from the *Mūlādhāra-Çhakṛa* on its own and there will be *Kuṇḍalinī Jāgaran*. You will feel the rise within yourself and you will be blessed with the initiation of the divine energy in yourself.

Benefits:

- Regular practice of this *Prāṇāyām* has the capacity of cleansing all your innumerable *Nāḍīs*, which makes the body healthy, lustrous and strong.
- All kinds of diseases occurring due to the disturbance of *Vāta Dosha* like rheumatism, gout, diseases pertaining to urinary and reproductive organs are cured. Besides, regular practice of this *Prāṇāyām* also cures diseases like cold, cataract, sinus, etc. which have reached a chronic stage. The three *Doṣas of Vāta*, *Pitta* and *Kapha* regularise themselves and assume proper proportions.
- Blockages in the arteries of the heart are removed and the arteries become clean, making the circulation unimpeded. If this *Prāṇāyām* is practiced for 3 to 4 months regularly, 30 to 40% of blockages in the arteries are dissolved and removed, preventing the risk of a heart attack.
- Pathogenic cholesterol, triglycerides, H.D.L. and L.D.L. also get controlled, making the arterial channels clear for effective and unimpeded flow of blood in the heart.
- Negative thinking is replaced by positive approach to life. It increases enthusiasm and spirit. The *sādhaka* becomes fearless and feels blissful.

In short, this *Prāṇāyām* has the effect of cleansing the body, and the mind and cures almost all the diseases from which the *sādhaka* has been suffering. If this *Prāṇāyām* is practiced for 250 to 500 times a day, *Kuṇḍalinī Shakti* turns its face upward and begin to rise above through the *Suṣhumṇā Nāḍī*. It means that the phenomenon known as *Kuṇḍalinī Jāgaran* begins.

Note:

- For more information see the chapter entitled "Methods and Precautions of *Kuṇḍalinī Jāgaran*".

Fifth Method - *Bhrāmarī Prāṇāyām*

Breathe in till your lungs are full of air. Close your ears with both the thumbs and eyes with the middle fingers of your hands on respective sides with little pressure. Press forehead with both the index fingers lightly. Close both the eyes. Then press eyes and nose bridge from the sides with the remaining fingers. Concentrate your mind on *Ājñā Çhakra* (between eye-brows) (See picture no. 4). Close your mouth. Begin slowly exhaling, making humming sound of a bee, while reciting "*OM*" mentally. Repeat the exercise 11 to 21 times according to your capacity.

Shiva Saṇkalpa (Vow) at the time of performing *Bhrāmarī Prāṇāyām:*

This *Prāṇāyām* should be done with the thought that your individual consciousness merges with the divine cosmic consciousness. Your mind should be full of the thought that divine bliss is descending on you, that deep divine wisdom fills your entire being. Exercising this *Prāṇāyām* with such thought will endow you with divine light and you will be able to meditate effortlessly.

Benefits :

- With the practice of this *Prāṇāyām* the mind becomes steady. It is beneficial in conditions like mental tension, agitation, high blood pressure, heart disease etc. It is also useful for meditation.

Sixth Method - *"Omkār Japa"*

(Muttering the *manṭra "OM"*)

After performance of the six *Prāṇāyām*s mentioned above, concentrate your mind on the respiration and meditate on the sacred *manṭra "OM"*. God has fashioned the shape of our brows like *OM*. This body and the universal cosmic body are filled with this *manṭra*. It is not the figure or expression of any individual thing, but it is divine energy, which regulates the entire functioning of the universe. With every act of breathing in and breathing out, mentally go on repeating the *manṭra "OM"*. The speed of respiration should be so slow and subtle that you yourself also may not be aware of its sound, even if a piece of cotton is placed in front of the nostril it should not move by the effect of the air exhaled out. Slowly practice and make the duration of one inhalation and exhalation to one minute. Likewise, try to visualize the breath inside the body. Initially the breath can be felt only in the nostrils but gradually it will be felt deep inside. In this way, visualizing the breath and continuous chanting of *'OM'* will lead to *Dhyāna* automatically. Your mind will develop a feeling of concentration and your body will be filled with the feeling of *OM*. The *Gāyatrī Manṭra* from the *Vedas* can also be chanted meaningfully along with *Prāṇāyām*. This way the *Sādhaka* can attain the joyful stage of *Samādhi* by going through the various visualizations of God and supreme powers. Also if this is practiced at bedtime, one will get peaceful sleep without any perverted dreams etc.

Seventh method - *Nāḍī Shōdhan Prāṇāyām*

Initially close the right nostril as you are told to do in the case of *Anuloma-Viloma Prāṇāyām*. Inhale slowly through the left nostril as deeply as possible. Retain the inhaled air according to your capacity. Do *'Mūlabandhā'* and *'Jālandhara bandhā'* simultaneously. After keeping yourself in this position unlock *Jālandhara Bandhā* and breathe out completely but slowly through the right nostril. Keep your breath out for sometime and then inhale slowly through the right nostril. Retain the inhaled air for sometime and then breathe out through the left nostril slowly but thoroughly. Repeat this exercise as many times as you consistently can. This *Prāṇāyām* is for cleansing the *Çhakras* and the *Nāḍīs*. If it is practiced without using hands on the nostrils then it increases concentration and is more beneficial, because one fully concentrates on the breath and the mind becomes totally stable and is under control. There should not be any sound while inhaling or exhaling. This should be done at least thrice and upto as many times one feels like doing it. Initially the ratio of *Pūrak, Antaḥ Kuṃbhak* and *Rēchak* should be kept as 1:2:2 i.e. if *Pūrak* is done for 10 seconds then *Antaḥ Kuṃbhak* (internal Kuṃbhak) should be done for 20 seconds and *Rēchak* should be done slowly for another 20 seconds. Later on the ratio may be changed to 1:4:2. After having done this, *Bāhaya Kuṃbhak* (external Kuṃbhak) can also be included in this and the ratio will be 1:4:2:2 for *Pūrak,*

Antaḥ Kuṃbhak, *Rēchak* and *Bāhaya Kuṃbhak* respectively.

This should be done at an extremely slow pace. Keeping in mind the count of *Prāṇas*, it should be done gradually. The slower the speed of *Prāṇa* the better it will be, inhaling at will, holding and then exhaling at will, is the actual criteria for the success of this *Prāṇāyām.* If done in this manner the need to take rest in between does not arise. While doing *Pūrak*, *Kuṃbhak* and *Rēchak* the chanting of *Om* and *Gāyatrī manṭra* should be done in the mind.

Benefits:

- The benefits of this *Prāṇāyām* are similar to that of *Anulom-Vilom Prāṇāyām*.

Other *Prāṇāyāms* useful in curing diseases

1. '*Sūrya-bhedī* or *Sūryāng*' *Prāṇāyām*:

Sit in any comfortable *āsana* as fit for meditation. Breathe in by the right nostril. Do '*Mūlabandhā*' and '*Jālandharabandhā*' with *Kuṃbhak*. Exhale through the left nostril. Increase the time duration of *Kuṃbhak*. Gradually with practice the *Prāṇāyām* and *Bandhās* can be done without any strain. Repeat the exercise gradually increasing from 3, 5, 7 to 10 times. When doing *Kuṃbhak* meditate on the solar system with all its luster. Reduce the number of this *Prāṇāyām* in summer season.

Benefits :

- It increases body-heat. It is beneficial in curing diseases caused by*Vāta* and *Kapha Doṣas* like intestinal worms, leprosy, gonorrhoea, different kinds of contagious diseases, indigestion and several diseases of the females. It is helpful in *Kuṇḍalinī Jāgaran*. It retards the process of aging. After doing *Anulom-Vilom Prāṇāyām* it should not be done for long durations. Doing *Sūrya-bhedī Prāṇāyām* without *Kuṃbhak* increases the activity of the heart and the stamina of the body. It also reduces the weight. It should be done 27 times, twice a day.

2. '*Çandṛabhēdī* or *Çaṇḍṛāṇg*' *Prāṇāyām* :

Sit in a comfortable *āsana*. Inhale through the left nostril and do *Kuṃbhak*. It is more beneficial to do this *Prāṇāyām* along with *Mūlabandhā* and *Jālandharabandhā*. Then exhale through the right nostril. In this *Prāṇāyām Pūrak* has to be done through the left nostril and *rēchak* is to be done through the right nostril. The process in this *Prāṇāyām* is just opposite to *Sūrya-Bhedi Prāṇāyām*. While doing *Kuṃbhak* meditate on the moon and its soothing light. In winter season the number of performance of this *Prāṇāyām* should be reduced.

Benefits:

- The body becomes cool, fatigue is relieved and the mind

is calmed. It is beneficial in relieving the burning sensation due to increase of *Pitta Doṣa*.

3. *'Ujjāyī Prāṇāyām'*:

Sit in an *āsana* in which you meditate. Contract the muscles of your throat as much as you can while doing *Pūrak* and when air is inhaled with the contracted throat muscles there occurs a sound similar to snoring. While sitting in *Dhyāna āsana* inhale air through both the nostrils. On doing so the air should touch the muscles of the contracted throat, but there should not be any friction in the nostrils. In the beginning do not do *Kuṃbhak* and do *Pūrak-Rēchak* only. After practice of some days, *Kuṃbhak* should be done for twice the time taken in *Purak* and *Rēchak*. If you do *Kuṃbhak* at both the stages for 10 seconds, perform *Jalandharbandhā* and *Mūlabandhā* simultaneously. In this *Prāṇāyām*, keep the right side nostril closed and exhale only through the left nostril.

Benefits:

- It is beneficial for those who suffer from cough, cold and bronchitis throughout the year. It is good for those who suffer from tonsillitis, thyroid, insomnia, mental tension, high blood pressure, constipation, *Vāta* diseases, tuberculosis etc. Its regular practice helps in getting rid of throat diseases and gives a sweet voice to the individual practicing it. This *Prāṇāyām* is also good for *Kuṇḍalinī Jāgaran*, *Ajapā-Japa Dhyāna* (chanting of the *mantra* in the mind soundlessly) etc. It cures lisping in children.

4. *'Karṇa-Rogāntaka Prāṇāyām'* :

Breathe in through both the nostrils as much as you can. Close both the nostrils. Shut the mouth. Try to breathe out the air through closed mouth as if you are attempting to expel the air through your ears. Push the breath upwards four to five times, then breathe out through both the nostrils. Repeating this 2 to 3 times will be sufficient.

Benefits:

- This *Prāṇāyām* is helpful in curing deafness and other diseases related to the ears.

5. '*Śītalī Prāṇāyām*':

Sit in a comfortable *āsana*. Place your palms on the knees of their respective sides. Bend the tongue from its extreme ends so as to form a cylindrical shape. Inhale through the tongue filling the lungs with air to their maximum capacity. Retain the air in *Kuṃbhak* as long as you can with *Jālandhara*bandh*ā*. Then close the mouth and exhale through the nostrils. Repeat again from first stage to last as many times as possible (8 to 10 times preferably). In winters it should not be practiced for a long duration.

Note:

Jālandharabandhā can also be used alongwith the *Kuṃbhak*. *Śītalī* and *Sītkārī Prāṇāyām* should not be done by those who are suffering from *Kapha* and also the individuals who suffer from cold, cough or tonsilitis.

Benefits:

- It is beneficial in diseases of the throat. It also cures diseases like indigestion, fever and disorders of the spleen.
- It helps to establish control on thirst and hunger. This has been stated in the ancient books on *Yog*.
- It lowers high-blood pressure and is beneficial in diseases caused by imbalance of *Pitta doṣa*. It also purifies blood.

6. '*Śītkārī Prāṇāyām*':

Sit in a meditative *āsana*. Touch your palate with your tongue closely. Close both the jaws closely, keeping the lips open. Breathe in through the mouth in a way that the air passes in through the closed jaws making a sound of air being sipped in. Fill the lungs to their maximum capacity. Do *Jālandharabandhā* and retain the air in as long as you can. Then close the mouth and breathe out slowly through the nose unlocking the *bandhā*. Repeat the exercise in the same manner. Repeating it 8 to 10 times is sufficient. During winters this *Prāṇāyām* should not be done for long durations.

Note:

- This *Prāṇāyām* can be done even without *Jālandharabandhā* or *Kuṃbhak*.

- During the process of *Pūrak,* the teeth and the tongue should remain stable at one place.

Benefits:

- This *Prāṇāyām* has all the benefits of *Śītalī Prāṇāyām.*
- Diseases pertaining to teeth, pyorrhea, etc. and diseases pertaining to throat, mouth, nose, tongue etc. are cured.
- It helps in curing sleepiness, and lowers the body temperature.
- If done 50 to 60 times a day for a long time, it cures hypertension.

7. '*Mūrcchā Prāṇāyām*':

Close your eyes. Breathe in through both the nostrils. Raise your head and tilt it a little back so that your eyes are looking towards the sky. Retain the breath in *Aṇtaṛ Kuṃbhak.* Open the eyes and look up in the sky. Keep yourself in this position as long as you can. Close your eyes and come back to original position, breathing out slowly. Repeat all the steps stated above without break in between. Doing this exercise 5 times daily is sufficient.

Benefits:

- It is useful in curing headache, tremors, weakness of muscles etc. It helps in improving eyesight and memory. It also aids in *Kuṇḍalinī Jāgaran* and in *Dhyāna.*

8. '*Plāvini Prāṇāyām*':

This in a way is a method of cleansing the stomach by filling air in it and exhaling it out forcefully. Inhale through the nostrils, as one would drink water, till the stomach is full and bulges out like a balloon. Retain the air in as long as you can and move the abdominal cavity as if you are belching or as in eructation. The air will move about in the whole abdominal cavity. Then exhale with as much force as you can so that all the contaminated air is thrown out through the mouth, like water is vomited out.

Benefits:

- It cures almost all diseases of the abdominal organs and

hysteria also. Abdominal parasites i.e. all kind of worms are killed or expelled and digestion improves. Contaminated and harmful air is expelled out of the body.

9. *'Kēvalī Prāṇāyām':*

Sit in a comfortable *āsana*. Inhale from both the nostrils slowly with the mental recitation of '*OM*', and then exhale. While inhaling, your concentration should be on the letter '*AU*' and while exhaling concentration should be on the letter '*M*'. Hence one breath (in and out) will be completed with the mental recitation of the *manṭra* '*OM*'. There is a continuous chanting of '*OM*'.

Benefits:

- It helps in improving *Dhyāna* and *Ajapā-japa* (Silent incantation of *manṭras*) is established.

Çhaķras or Energy Centres of the *Prāṅic* Body

Çhaķras are the energy centers of various kinds located in our *Prāṅic* body, regulating the functioning of the vital organs of the physical body by providing the energy needed by them. These *Çhaķras* commence from the root of the spinal cord up to the top of the head. In normal condition their appearance is like an undeveloped lotus turned upside-down stem above and petals below. These *Çhaķras* are awakened and bloom to their fullest capacity by observance of Yogic exercises like celibacy, *Prāṇāyām* and *Dhyāna* etc. Then their divine inner power begins to develop and is exhibited in various ways. Pictures of these *Çhaķras* given in this book are symbolic and have been incorporated to give an idea of their subtle nature. Even their English names such a "Pelvic Plexus" etc. do not represent their real location but give only a hint or rough idea regarding their location in the body.

Brief description of the *Çhaķras*:

This is what God says about *Çhaķras* in *Athaŗva-Vēda:*

> ***Aṣṭa-cakrā nava-dvārā devānāṃ pūrayodhyā***
> ***Tasyāṃ hiraṇyayaḥ kośaḥ svargo jyotiṣāvṛtaḥ***
>
> **(*Athaŗva-Vēda*)**

The city of God Ayodhya is represented in this body by eight *Çhaķras* and nine gates (two eyes, two nostrils, two ears, mouth, organs of reproduction and anus.) The city of Gods is illuminated by the golden rays, and is the abode of eternal peace, happiness and celestial pleasures. A *yogi* who follows the tenets of the science of *Yog* becomes capable of achieving this celestial treasure and enjoys it till eternity. Let us now describe these *Çhaķras* briefly.

1. *Mūlādhāra- Çhaķra* (Pelvic Plexus):

This *Çhaķra* is situated at a place two fingers above the perineum and two fingers below the genital organs. From its center emerges the *Suşhumṇā Nāḍī*. From its left side originates the *Iḍā Nāḍī* and the *Piṅgalā Nāḍī* from its right; therefore it is called *Triveṇī* (confluence of three *Nāḍīs*) also. Since it is the root place where the *Kuṇḍalinī* has its abode, it is called '*Mūlādhāra Çhakṛa*'. Concentration on this *Çhakṛa* brings to the *sādhaka* benefits like health, vigour and capacity to perform even the most difficult tasks. On the awakening of this *Çhakṛa* the appearance of the *sādhaka* becomes luminous, virile and is elevated to higher dimensions. He also becomes free from all bodily ailments. Picture No. 5 illustrates that this *Çhakṛa* is illuminated by the Sun, with the effulgent rays of cosmic intellect. It is the place from which soft and delightful light as from a torch emanates and is spread around, illuminating the entire field reaching up to the *Swadhisthan Çhakṛa*. Control of *Prāṇa*, through the Yogic exercise of *Dhāraṇā* and *Dhyāna* removes all the darkness enveloping the *Mūlādhāra Çhakṛa* and illuminates it so as to push aside the dross elements revealing its subtle nature. This is called *Kuṇḍalinī Jāgaran*.

Picture No. (5) in this book shows parts of the physiology including it's *Prāṅic* aspects. S.No. 1 indicates '*Suṣhumṇā*' at the top. S.No. 2 indicates the lower part of the abdomen connected with this *Çhakṛa*. S.No. 3 indicates the intestines depicted in rosy colour. S.No. 4 indicates large intestines in yellow colour. S.No. 5 indicates the rectum and anus. S.No. 6 indicates the coccyx, the lower most end of the spinal cord. S.No. 7 indicates the lowest part of *Suṣhumṇā Nāḍī*. S.No. 8 indicates the lower part of *Suṣhumṇā*'s principal expansion and S.No. 9 indicates the illuminated *Mūlādhāra- Çhakṛa*.

2. *Svādhiṣthāna Çhakṛa* (Hypogastric Plexus) :

About two fingers above the Muladhar *Çhakṛa* is situated the *Svādhiṣthāna Çhakṛa*. In the treatise on *Tantra t*his *Çhakṛa* is shown to have been associated with nature's activities like creation, maintenance and destruction. It is also endowed with the faculty of instant knowledge. Prodigies who are endowed with the capacity of unfailing memory for several things simultaneously belong to the category of those in whom the *Svādhiṣthāna Çhakṛa* is very active.

A look at the picture no. 6, will show that this *Çhakṛa* is located in the lower part of the abdomen, and covers organs like kidneys, urethra, ureters, i.e. the urinary system, organs of reproduction and prostate gland etc. These include (1) left and right kidneys, (2) Urinary organs, (3) Hind portion of the Urinary organ, (4) Urinary ducts coming out from the kidneys, which are entering Urinary organs as at (2) and are embedding in it. In the same *Çhakra* itself there is another place included in which the green leaves (5) are the places where semen is stored, ducts for carrying semen are on both left and right, (6) are the organs for semen formation (testicles), (7) are the prostrate glands through which ducts carrying semen and urine pass by, (8) is the penis. By going through this *Çhakra* one gets a fair idea of the functioning of the Urinary and Reproductive Systems and their interconnection with each other.

3. *Maṇipūra Çhakra* (Epigastric Plexus or Solar Plexus):

This *Çhakra* has its location in the navel region. It covers all the organs of the digestive system including vital organs like pancreas. This *Çhakra* energises the digestive system. In *Yog-Darśana*'s percept *'Naabhichakre Kaayvyuhgyaanam'* (3.29), it is said that concentration on this *Çhakra* endows the *sādhaka* with encyclopedic knowledge about the parts of the body. Its awakening has the effect of curing diseases like diabetes; constipation, indigestion, flatulence etc. All the other abnormalities relating to digestion are eradicated.

Picture no. 7 gives an idea about the location of this *Çhakra*. It is located behind the navel. This *Çhakra* includes (1) stomach, (2) liver, (3) spleen, (4) pancreas, (5) duodenum.

4. *Anāhata Çhakra* (Cardiac Plexus):

This *Çhakra* is located near the heart. In religious books on *Taṇtra*, this *Çhakra* is shown to be associated with the functions of speech, ability to compose poetry and ability to have control over one's sense organs. *Shivsaar Taṇtra* says, that the *Anāhata* sound *(Naad)* emanating from this *Çhakra* is for welfare, and it helps the individual in progress from *Dhāraṇā* to *Dhyāna*. It is believed that if ladies and *sādhaka*s having faith in their heart, concentrate regularly on this *Çhakra*, they will never ever suffer from any heart disease.

Picture No. 8 shows the enlarged view of the *Anāhata Çhakra*. In this, the middle circles in the shape of a white lotus which appear to be located in the heart have been clearly indicated.

5. *Hṛdaya Çhakṛa* or *Niṃn-Manāś Çhakṛa* (Lower Mind Plexus):

This *Çhakṛa* is located in the middle of the two breasts. By concentration on this *Çhakṛa* divine qualities like dispassionate love, compassion, sympathy for the suffering etc. develop in the individual who practices it. Maharishi Vyas also recommends the practice of concentration on this *Çhakṛa*. This is not a physical part of the body but it is emotional It is very sensitive and is related to the mind of the person. See picture no. 9 for its location.

6. *Viśuddhi Çhakṛa* (Carotid Plexus):

This *Çhakṛa* is situated in the region of the throat. When awakened by constant concentration, it makes the aspirant poetic, very learned, calm minded and healthy. He becomes free from the feelings of sorrow and his lifespan is increased. Due to awakening of this *Çhakṛa* abnormalities of the thyroid glands never occur. In the picture no. 10 *Viśuddhi Çhakṛa* has been described, in which the organs shown as 'A' are related to the following numbers viz. (1) trachea, (2) & (3) both the lungs, (4) the internal parts of the lungs.

7. *Ājñā Çhakṛa* (Madula Plexus):

This *Çhakṛa* is located between the two eyebrows. It is related to two very important glands; pituitary and pineal glands. On awakening of this *Çhakṛa* these two glands become very active and the person in whose case this happens gains considerable intelligence. By the exercise of *Kapāla-bhāti*, *Anulom-Vilom* and *Nāḍī Shōdhan Prāṇāyāms,* the mind becomes composed and unwavering and begins to reach the stage of *Sampragnyata Samādhi* (concentration of one-pointed mind). From the *Mūlādhāra- Çhakṛa*, the *Iḍā*, *Piṅgalā* and *Suṣhumṇā Nāḍīs* take an upward-course separately but ultimately meet at the place of this *Çhakṛa*. For this reason this *Çhakṛa* is also known as *Triveṇī* i.e. as place where three *Nāḍī*s meet. This plexus looks like two balls and is shown in part 'B' of picture no. 10. The light in the upward direction on the forehead is that of *Suṣhumṇā Nāḍī*.

Iḍā bhāgīrathī gaṅgā piṅgalā yamunā nāḍī
Tayormadhyagatā nāḍī Suṣhumṇākhyā Sarasvatā
Triveṇī saṅgamo yatra tirtharājaḥ sa ucyate
Tatra snānaṃ prakurvīta sarva-pāpaiḥ pramucayate
(*Gyana Saṅkalinī Taṇtra*)

Iḍā Nāḍī is compared to river *Gaṅgā*, *Piṅgalā Nāḍī* is compared to river *Yamunā* and *Suṣhumṇā Nāḍī* is compared to river *Sarasvatā*. The *Triveṇī of* the three rivers are considered to be most sacred, and *Prayāga* the place where these three rivers meet is considered to be the most holy place of pilgrimage. It is believed that a bath taken at this place, washes away all the sins of the man who takes the holy dip. But in Yogic terminology this confluence takes place, not anywhere outside, but inside our body. The belief that a dip in *Prayāga*, at the place of confluence of the three rivers, extricates a person from all the sins committed by him is false and illusory. Since, if it were so, a murderer, after committing the heinous crime of murdering a *Ḅraḥmin*, a *Gurū* or his brother would be able to get rid of his sins, just by bathing at this place, but this does not happen. Sin means crime, which causes harm to others. So each one has to face the consequences of his sins. If one does good acts after committing sins, then also he has to face the consequences for both his acts separately i.e. for the sin and for the good acts he has done. That is why it has been said in the scriptures that: "*Avaśyameva bhoktavyaṃ kṛtaṃ karma śul*". If a person, with full faith takes a dip in the holy river *Gaṅgā* or at the *Triveṇī*, with the thought in mind that I will never ever commit sins in the remaining part of life, then because of his pure thoughts he can protect himself from the sins in future, but still he cannot save himself from the consequences of the sins that he has committed in the earlier part of his life. This is what is known about the external *Triveṇī*, but if anyone concentrates on the *Ājñā Çhaḳra* and the *Triveṇī* therein by way of *Prāṇāyām* and *Dhyāna* and concentrates on the worship of god, takes a dip in the *Gaṅgā* of knowledge, then the desires of committing sins vanishes. Then the person does not even think about sin. Therefore, if one wants to attain liberation, then he should daily perform *Yogāḅḥyā*sa while chanting '*OM*' while concentrating the mind fully on the *Ājñā Çhaḳra*.

8. *Saḥsrār Çhakṛa* (Cerebral Gland) :

This *Çhakṛa* is located at the crown of the head inside the brain, above the *Brahmarandhra* (an aperture supposed to be at the crown of the head through which the souls of virtuous and sinless persons or yogis pass away at the time of the death of their physical bodies) and is the centre for all divine powers. By concentration of the mind and *Prāṇa* at this place, mental fluctuations, *Vipaṛyaya* (False knowledge), *Vikalpa* (all kinds of illusions), *Nidra* (conditions analogous to sleep) and *Smriti* (past memories etc.) are brought under control; and the *sādhaka* attains the stage of *Asaṃpṛagyāt Samādhi* (which is a stage higher than the stage of *Saṃpṛagyāt Samādhi* in which the soul soars beyond the three *Guṇas-Saṭva*, *Rajaṣ* and *Tamaṣ*).

Those who are learned and have experienced various stages of *Yog* say that the description of *Hṛdaya-Puruśa* which is given in *Upaniṣads* shows that the *Saḥsrār Çhakṛa* is in *Ḅraḥmaranḍhra* which is about the size of the thumb. Since this is the abode of super mental power *Çhitta* having its abode in *Ākāsha*, it is here that soul consciousness is reflected. It is this *Çhitta*, which illuminates the mind of the *sādhaka* with celestial knowledge.

So many people ask: Where is the abode of the soul? This is a difficult question to answer. However, if we devote a little thought to this question, we come to the conclusion that the knowledge of the soul casts its illuminative reflection on the *Çhitta. Çhitta* is the causal body. For this reason its association with the physical body is known as *Jīvātman* (that which animate the physical body or individual or personal soul). Causal body permeates the etheric subtle body, which in turn permeates the physical body. In this way, this occupies every cell of the physical body. Still however, on account of different functions it performs, it is given different names suggestive of its locations and functions.

Ordinarily, in the sleep state it resides in the region of the heart, since the heart is the principal center of the body. It is from here that innumerable *Nāḍīs*, are spread in the entire body. Central control of the body is in the heart from which all the *Nāḍīs* are provided energy and inner or involuntary functions of the body are guided from here. Once the heart stops, functioning of the entire body comes to a stand still. It is for this reason that the abode of the soul is shown to be in the heart, particularly during sleeping stage when the consciousness is in suspension. As described in the *Upanishad*:

Yatraiṣa etat supto' bhūd ya eṣa vijñānamayaḥ puruṣastadeṣāṃ
Vijñānena vijñānamādāya ya eṣo 'ntarhṛdaya ākāśastasmiñchete
(*Bṛhadāraṇyaka Upa.* 2/1/17)

When this soul, which is scientific, is asleep, then it rests along with the science of these sense organs at the place, where ether is located in the heart.

In the dreaming state, the abode of soul is believed to be in the throat, since all impressions gathered in the waking state are believed to have been located in a tiny *Nāḍī* known as *Hitā Nāḍī*, which has the dimension equal to 1/1000th part of a hair. Hence, the impressions of the objects experienced in the waking state leave their mark in a subtle form in the region of the throat. In the waking state the soul comes in contact with worldly things through the sense organs. From amongst these sense organs 'eyes' are the most important, therefore, the state of abode of the soul in the awakened state is believed to be located in the eyes.

Ya eshoakshini purusho drashyat esh aatmeti
(*Chaando*, 8.7.4)

Chhāandgyo Upaniṣad declares that the *Puruśa*, which is seen in the eyes, is the 'Soul'. In the stage of *Saṃpragyāt Samādhi*, the abode of soul is believed to be in *Ājñā Çhakra*, since it is the place of divine vision. It is also called *Divya Neṭra* or *Śhiva Neṭra*. In *Saṃpragyāt Samādhi* the abode of soul is *Ḅraha-raṇḍhra*, it is at this place where due to stabilisation of *Prāṇa* and mind the state of *Asaṃpragyāt* is achieved i.e. restriction on all the repetitions takes place. In the picture no. 10, at the point 'B' (1) is *Suṣhumṇā* head, (2) is the little-brain, (3) surrounded by the *Pañchatanmatra* circle, mind + brain + *Vijñānamaya Kośa* or *Śukśma-Śarīra* is the collection of 10 sense organs. (4) *Braḥa raṇḍhra* (*Saḥsrār*), (5) is the part of internal brain, here the 3 red spots are known as '*Ahīpati-raṇḍhra*'.

Symbolic *Vēdic* Names of the *Çhaķras*

In *Vēdic* literature, the *Vēdic* names of all the *Çhaķras* viz. *Mūlādhāra Çhaķra* etc., are in the form of seven supermystic names viz. *Bhūh', 'Bhuvaḥ'* etc. *'Bhūh', 'Bhuvaḥ'* etc. are the forms of the seven Acharyas of *Yog*. In the terminology of *Yog* '*Bhuh*' is said to mean or represent *Mūlādhāra Çhaķra*, '*Bhuvaḥ*' represents *Svādhiṣthāna Çhaķra*, 'Ṣvaḥ' means *Maṇipūra Çhaķra*, '*Mahah*' means *Anāhata Çhaķra, 'Janaḥ'* means *Viśuddhi Çhaķra, 'Tapaḥ*' means *Ājñā Çhaķra* and *'Saṭyam'* means *Saḥsrār Çhaķra*. These *Çhaķras,* possess their own respective energies and light, but they are still affected by the light emitted by *Prāṇamaya* (Etheric), *Manomaya (*Mental) and *Vijñānamaya* (Mental body) *Kośas* also. If any of these *Kośas* suffer from any eclipse due to any reason whatsoever, the practice of *Prāṇāyām* removes the eclipse and enables the *Çhaķras* to illuminate with full splendour.

Kuṇḍalinī Śhakti

The cosmic energy which has its abode in *Mūlādhāra- Çhakra* is described in *Vēdic* literature *as Lord Ḅraḥma's abode*, and in the ancient *Tantrik* Literature as *Kuṇḍalinī Śhakti* (coiled as a serpent). Normally *Prāṇa Śhakti* i.e. life force flows through the *Iḍā* and *Piṅgalā Nāḍīs*. However, when a person performs *Yog*, his cosmic energy lying dormant in the *Suṣhumṇā Nāḍī* begins to develop, move and takes an upward course. Earlier this was giving energy to the organs of the body to enjoy the pleasures of life. Even philosophers like Pythagoras and Plato also have stated that there is some cosmic force in the body of every human being located in the navel region, which enlightens the brain, resulting in the development of divine energy in man.

Çhakṛa Shōdhan or *Kuṇḍalinī Jāgaran* (Awakening of Serpentine Energy)

'Yaḥ piṇde saḥ ḅraḥmāndē' — which means that it is unanimously believed that the energy, which pervades the entire universe, pervades the smallest units of the world including the human body. The base of this energy is located in *Mūlādhāra- Çhakṛa*. On purification and awakening of this *Çhakṛa*, a divine energy takes an upward course. This is called *Kuṇḍalinī Jāgaran.* The effect of *Kuṇḍalinī Jāgaran* is that it works like a power station, where power is generated and supplied to different places, which are connected by wires to the power station. When the main switch is turned 'ON' the supply begins and when it is put 'OFF' the supply stops. Similar to that, when the *Kuṇḍalinī Śhakti* is awakened other *Çhakṛas* are activated and enlightened automatically.

When this *Kuṇḍalinī Śhakti* begins to take an upward course, the *Çhakṛas* coming in its way also turn their faces upwards and become more active. When this energy reaches the place where *Ājñā Çhakṛa* is located the *sādhaka* attains the stage of *Samprajñāta Samādhi* and when it reaches *Saḥsrār Çhakṛa*, the *sādhaka* reaches the stage of *Asamprajñāta Samādhi* and all the fluctuations of the mind become still and equipoised. In such a condition the soul begins to realise the divine knowledge, which is already there in the *Çhitta* in a germ form. This stage is called *'Ritambhara Prājñā'* (Pure, unalloid knowledge) On acquisition of this knowledge the *sādhaka* attains the final and most comprehensive truth about the entire universe. Nothing then remains to be known by him. On reaching this stage, the *sādhaka* begins to experience *Nirbīja Samādhi* and enjoys its endless and all pervading bliss. This is the highest stage of *Yog*. When the *sādhaka* reaches this stage all his passions for worldly pleasures retire and he becomes free from the cycle of births and deaths, a stage of eternal bliss that is called *Niṛvāna* in Buddhism and *Mokśa* in *Vēdic* philosophy.

Methods of *Kuṇḍalinī Jāgaran*

In the *Siḍdha Yog* tradition *Kuṇḍalinī Jāgaran* is brought about by a method known as *Śhakti-pāta* (Transference of Energy). If one happens to be in contact of a virtuous sage experienced in Yogic methods, his strong resolve may result in the passage of divine energy into the body of the *sādhaka*, who goes deep into meditation, without any efforts on his part. But meeting such an accomplished and experienced sage is very rare. Therefore, in the present times *Kuṇḍalinī Jāgaran* by methods advocated by *Haṭh Yog* assume great importance. Gorakhanathji, a proponent of *Haṭh Yog* has given description of nine *Çhaḳras* in *'Siḍdha Siḍdhānta Paḍdhati'*. In *Haṭh-Yog* also the meditation is to be performed by concentrating on the six *Çhaḳra* i.e. *Mūlādhāra Çhaḳra*, *Swadhisthan Çhaḳra*, *Maṇipūra Çhaḳra*, *Anāhata Çhaḳra*, *Viśuddhi Çhaḳra* and *Ājñā Çhaḳra*. By piercing these *Çhaḳras*, the *sādhaka* can have a glimpse of Shiva, the creator of this universe in the *Saḥsrār Çhaḳra*. In achieving this end the body is purified by six body purifying methods, *Āsanas*, *Prāṇāyām*, *Mudras* and *Bandhās* etc. *Çhaḳras*, which are soiled with unwanted dirty material, can be rendered clean by *Prāṇāyām* only. On purification of the channels of energy by the control of breath the *sādhaka* acquires the capacity of withdrawing his *Çhitta* from the subjects of the sense organs and becomes absolutely introvert. By meditation, his mind becomes immobile and, stops all kind of fluctuations. Such a situation being attained the *sādhaka* becomes capable of controlling the five elements i.e. Prthvi,

Jal, *Vāyu*, *Agni* and *Ākāsha* of which the human body and the whole universe is constituted. On piercing the *Çhaķras*, when *Kuṇḍalinī* reaches *Saḥsrār Çhaķra*, the soul realizes Lord *Shiva*. The highest achievement of *Haṭh-Yog* is the realisation of *Shiva*, through *Kuṇḍalinī Jāgaran*. And this also is the final aim of everyone's life.

When the *sādhaka* acquires stability in an *āsana* selected by him, he is able to acquire proficiency in meditation and intense concentration in which he establishes identity with the Supreme Being, the creator of this universe. When the *sādhaka* sits in a meditative *āsana* with his spine straightened up, the cosmic energy easily flows through the bunch of subsidiary channels emerging from *Suṣhumṇā Nāḍī*. However, if the *sādhaka* is not able to sit with his spine straight the muscles contract, resulting in the contamination of subsidiary channels by collection of *Kapha* and other useless material present in the body and this obstructs the even flow of energy through these channels and as a result of this the subsidiary channels remain eclipsed by the toxins. Such a situation also obstructs the flow of *Prāṅic* energy through respiration. By the practice of *Prāṇāyām* the uneven flow of *Prāṇa* is corrected and the *sādhaka* attains equanimity. The practice of meditation of *Prāṇāyām* causes indelible effect on the *Prāṇmaya Kośa* of the aspirant, with the result that all the parts of the *Prāṇmaya Kośa* get stimulated, circulation of blood improves and the elements like phlegm etc. get dissolved rendering vital organs like lungs, skin and intestines clean. As a result of this, a strange phenomenon happens and a kind of thrilling sensation is experienced in the body. In Yogic terminology, it is known as *Pranothana* (the rising of the *Prāṇas*) which is the first step in the direction of *Kuṇḍalinī Jāgaran*. In this, the *sādhaka* experiences a dynamic touch, in which due to movement in *Prāṇa*, strange phenomenons related to touch start. By constant and regular practice, some light is visible in some places in the body and in the final stage, the *Kuṇḍalinī* begins to emerge. In this way by establishing control on the movement of the *Prāṇa* by *Prāṇāyām*, one comes in close proximity of *Prāṇamaya Kośa*. As a matter of fact, all the *Pañcha-Kośas* are controlled by the *Prāṇa*. The contamination of *Çhaķras* and the dross, which covers them, is removed by the practice of *Prāṇāyām*. This results in the efficient working of the *Çhaķras* and unimpeded supply of energy to the entire body and the *sādhaka* is able to visualize in-time, the processes going on in the *Çhakṛas*, their energies, the various *Prāṇas* which are working in various parts of the body, sub-*Prāṇas*, Gods and Lords located therein. With regular practice of *Prāṇa Sadhna*, there develops control over the power of the *Çhakṛas* that controls it, then he is able to guide the *Prāṅic* energy right from the *Mūlādhāra- Çhakṛa* to *Saḥsrār Çhakṛa* in a manner desired by him. There develops an ability to easily visualize all the *Çhakṛas* and the all the layers under the layers of the next *Kośas*. Picture no.11 displays that by regular practice of *Prāṇāyām*, the entire web of *Nāḍīs* and the entire course of *Suṣhumṇā* and *Prāṇa*, is illuminated and motivated. '*Buddhi*' (the main part of the *Sūkṣam Sharir* is situated in the forehead) (1) mind motivated by it, (2) its light '*Suṣhumṇā*'- in the head, (3) is passing through the course is all the'*Nāḍī-Yugal'* (pairs of energy channels), (5) illuminating it is, *Mūlādhāra Çhakṛa* (4) which is flowing through it.

By regular practice of *Prāṇāyām* with devotion, the darkness slowly fades, and all the *Çhakṛas* start getting illuminated viz. *Mūlādhāra Çhakṛa, Swadhishtan Çhakṛa* and the *Saḥsrār Çhakṛa* located on top. In picture no.12 it is attempted to give a glimpse of the *Çhakṛas* before their illumination by *Prāṇāyām*. The lowest of them is the *Mūlādhāra- Çhakṛa*, it can be compared to a *HOMA-KUNḌ-SUM* (a quadrangular place built with bricks for making offerings) and on the top is located the *Svādhiṣthāna Çhakṛa*. Above it is located the Maṇipūra *Çhakṛa*. All these *Çhakṛas* are stuffed and surrounded by countless *Nāḍīs*, emitting the sacred sound of *OM*. Above the *Maṇipūra Çhakṛa*, in the chest region is the *Anāhata Çhakṛa*, which is illuminated by the *DEEPA-ŚHIḲHĀ-SUM*. In the throat region is located throat the *Viśuddhi Çhakṛa*, and above it, between the two eyebrows, in the forehead is located the *Ājñā Çhakṛa* and at the top in the head region (crown) is located the *Saḥsrār Çhakṛa*, which is illuminated like the Sun.

In the beginning of the Yogic exercise, the *sādhaka* becomes aware only of the crude form of these *Çhakṛas*, but with progress in the practice, meditation secrets of the entire body are revealed to him and the *sādhaka* acquires the capacity similar to the capability of a television to receive channels from all over the world, enabling him to visualize the entire universe. Picture no. 13 makes it clear – (1) In the Heart the soul is always illuminated and keeps the innerself illuminated, it inspires *Vijñānamaya Kośa* (4) through the course (5,6) and further inspires mind (3) by its rays (7) and making the inner sight (5) divine. By the strength of the vow of a *sādhaka,* the Divine Vision (5) by its own emission of rays (8) makes him visualize the objects located further than the Solar System and also (9) by penetrating deep inside the core of the planet earth.

These *Çhakras* are located at the base of the spinal cord in their germ form as illuminated in *Sushumṇā Nāḍī*. Picture no. 14 is an Illustration of the mystic *Sushumṇā Nāḍī*, in which (1) displays that this *Nāḍī* is made up of 33 vertebrae and is like a coiled serpent. In this, there lies the red coloured '*Sushumṇā*' which too is present like a coiled serpent. 'a' is the head of *Sushumṇā*, which is connected to the brain and 'b' is its tail, which is connected to the bone at tail end or anal end. (2) is clarifying the internal state of the *Sushumṇā* where – 'a'; is a pair of *Nāḍīs* coming out of the two vertebrae and spread out in the body. 'b' is the view clearly displaying the actual state of these paired *Nāḍīs* when the outer protection has been cut. 'c' is the confounded cut of the *Sushumṇā*. 'd' is the muscular cushion placed in middle of each of the pairs of vertebrae. 'e' – the pairs of *Nāḍīs* from 'a' to 'e' come out in this manner and spread out throughout the whole body.

At 'f' are the muscles on the back, which are attached centrally to all the vertebrae from top to bottom. In (3) and (4), the lateral cut view of the *Sushumṇā* is shown, where a web of *Nāḍīs* responsible for 'flow of knowledge' and 'flow of movement' in the body are displayed. These *Nāḍīs* are thinner than the threads of a cobweb. This web of *Nāḍīs* performs its functions continuously without any rest, not even for a second. In 5 the *Sushumṇā* and its two major *Nāḍīs* '*Iḍā*' and '*Piṅgalā*' located on its right and left side, come down by the sides and meet the bone at the anal end. The *Iḍā-Piṅgalā Nāḍīs* tied together by knots appear as a garland.

In the body, the *Sushumṇā* is the main medium by which all the activities related to propagation of life force made up of 'knowledge' and action combined together, take place.

A table giving the details of the *Çhakṛas* has been given on the next page, so that the readers may get important information about the *Çhakṛas* in a systematic manner.

From what is stated above, it becomes clear that with the awakening of *Mūlādhāra- Çhakṛa*, awakening of the other *Çhakṛas* also begins automatically, and the divine energy begins to take an upward course. This is called *Kuṇḍalinī Jāgaran*. In scientific terms *Kuṇḍalinī* can be described as the human-divine-light, which pervades the entire body. The aspirant who desires to do cleansing, piercing and awakening of the *Çhakṛa* should get the training by the methods given hereunder (under the guidance of a learned *Yog Sādhaka*).

- *Bhastrikā Prāṇāyām* in the morning and evening for 3 minutes, at both the times, and after this *Kapāla-bhāti Prāṇāyām* for at least 5 minutes must be done. In the beginning of the practice of *Kapāla-bhāti Prāṇāyām,* rest for a while in between. Approximately, after one month, you will be proficient in performing this *Prāṇāyām* for 5 minutes without any break in between.
- After doing *Bhastrikā* and *Kapāla-bhāti Prāṇāyām* perform *Bāhya Prāṇāyām* with *Tribandhā* for 11 times.
- After exercising these three *Prāṇāyām*s do *Anulom-Vilom Prāṇāyām* for 5 to 10 minutes to cleanse all the minor and major *Nāḍīs* (the number of these *Nāḍīs* is assessed to be 727,210,210) without any halt in between. If these *Prāṇāyām*s cannot be done twice, never miss to do it in the morning. Failure in doing so may result in a delay in achieving the goal.

  In the beginning, it is better to perform *Anulom-Vilom Prāṇāyām* with small pauses in between. Do the *Prāṇāyām* for one minute, pause for a few moments and rest; and then resume again. If done in this manner, in about a month or two you will acquire proficiency to do this *Prāṇāyām* for 5 to 10 minutes without any pause or rest. Remember that with every inhalation and exhalation it is necessary to do mental recitation of *OM*, because *Prāṇāyām* and meditation are closely interlinked. By the practice of *Prāṇāyām* even an unsteady mind becomes steady on its own. And if this condition is linked with the recitation of the sacred *manṭra* of *OM*, you gradually get the pleasure of *Dhyāna* and *Samādhi* both.

- After performance of the above stated practices, slowly begin to perform *Nāḍī Shodhan Prāṇāyām* without touching the nostrils. With each respiration mentally recite the manṭra *OM* with the understanding of its meaning. In this way, you must also do *Nāḍī Shōdhan Prāṇāyām* 3 to 11 times.
- The *Prāṇāyāms* indicated above should be done in accordance with the instructions given in the Chapter "Seven kinds of *Prāṇāyāms*" where detailed description of these *Prāṇāyāms* has been given.
- Lastly, with simultaneous concentration of the mind and *Prāṇa* try to look inside your body. In this way by doing *Prāṇāyām* with mental recital of *OM* regularly on a daily basis, you will be able to reach the highest pinnacles of *Yog*. This kind of *Japa-Dhyāna* (meditation with recital) generates sequential vibrations, which creates a strange tickling sensation in *Mūlādhāra- Çhaḳra*. These tickling sensations or pleasurable waves produce a *Naad* sound in the Navel due to creation of *Taṛrit*, an electrifying-vibration through *Prāṇmaya Kośa*. Due to this a special kind of the warmth is felt in the stomach. The warmth so produced in the stomach is converted to resolution. Because of the *Japa-Dhyāna* special kind of vibrations are produced which enter the *Prāṇmaya Kośa* in the form of electric-waves by the group of nerves. A flow starts from the brain and reaches the *Maṇipūra Çhaḳra* located in the navel and affects it.

The meaning of *Japa-Dhyāna* of *OM* is raising the *Prāṇa* from the lowest state to the highest state which lifts the mind from the activity region of the *Prāṇa* to the *Vijñānmaya Kośa*, and to stabilize it by bringing the mind-brain to the level of the *Ānaṇdamaya Kośa.* In other words, sequentially we can say that the body starting the practice of *Prāṇa* is crossing *Prāṇamaya*, *Manomaya* and *Vijñānmaya Kośas*, then gathering together the self-realisation spread throughout the body and bringing it to the heart, which is, stabilizing one's self or to stabilize in *Ānaṇdānugat* and *Aṣmitaṇugat Samādhis*.

Besides *Prāṇa Dhyāna*, *Dhyāna* can also be done for *Gāyatrī mantra*, the greatest mantra from the Vedas, as shown in Picture no. 15. As demonstrated in no. 3 in the picture, the *sādhaka* should try and look into his mind in the head with *Dhyāna* and try to visualize that a Divine Light is filling in the mind, and it is full, and focused like a torchlight (2), moonlight like white bright light from an heavenly abode is entering into one's golden-yellow brain. By enlightening of the intellect, which is the controlling authority of the *Vijñānmaya Kośa*, the mind the 'king of senses' and all the senses under its control are attaining purity on their own. It is then, that there exists waves of utmost peace and divine light, inside the mind and the heart, all through the day and night.

A *sādhaka* if he desires so, can also concentrate on the Divine Light instead of *Om* or *Gāyatrī Japa*, as shown in Picture no. 16. One can think that the lustrous *Sahaṣtrākśa* (God) (1) is showering *Bṛaḥmatej* (divine light) upon me and *Bṛaḥmatej* is shining like the Sun (2) in my heart and that God is with me in the form of the ultra-pure *Sauṃya Jyoti*, and is present in my soul (3). One should wish that this Divine Light illuminates my life and stays with me throughout my life.

The Various *Çhaķras*

Name of the *Çhaķras*	Physical Appearance	Location	Element	Germ	Principal *Prāņa*	Subsidiary *Sub-Prāņa*	*Kośa*	World/ Universe	Diseases that may be caused due to improper whirling of the *Çhaķras*
Mūlādhāra	Pelvic Plexus	Nearly 1" inside the center of genitals and anus	Earth	*Laṃ*	*Apāna*	*Kūrma*	*Aņnamaya*	*Bhūḥ*	Constipation, Diarrhea, vomiting
Svādhiṣṭhāna	Hypogastric Plexus	1"-1.5" above *Mūlādhāra Çhaķra*	Water	*Vaṃ*	*Vyāna*	*Dhanañjaya*	*Prāņamaya*	*Bhuvāḥa*	Insomnia, Stones
Maņipūra	Epigastric or Solar Plexus	Near the navel	Fire	*Raṃ*	*Samāna*	*Kŗkala*	*Manomaya*	*Şwaḥa*	Asthma, Arthritis, Piles, Weakness of bones
Anāhata	Cardiac Plexus	Heart	Air	*Yaṃ*	*Prāņa*	*Nāga*	*Vijñānamaya*	*Mahā*	Disorder of nervous system, Gastric problem, Unconsci-ousness, Arrogance
Hŗdaya Çhaķra or Manaś çhaķra	Lower Mind Plexus	In between both the breasts	This is not a physical part of the body, but emotional, related to the Heart.						
Viśuddhi	Carotid Plexus	Throat	Ether	*Haṃ*	*Udāna*	*Devdatta*	*Ānaņdamaya*	*Janaḥa*	Boils, Pimples, Tumors, Swelling, Pus formation, Diseases of eyes
Ājñā Çhaķra	Medula Plexus	Between the two eyebrows	Desire	*Om*				*Tapaḥa*	Dropsy, Diseases of respiratory system, Palpitation in the heart
Saḥsrār	Cerebral	Head	Intellect					*Saţyaṃ*	

Some Guidelines for *Dhyāna* (Meditation)

- While doing meditation treat it as the most important thing and devote exclusive attention to it. Do not pay attention to other thoughts, however important and sacred they may be. Giving alms, rendering service to others, altruism and benevolence, study of the sacred books, service of one's *Gurū*, service to one's own progeny etc., are of course pious acts, but thoughts on these subjects also should be kept aside when meditating.The target of meditation and the accompanying practices like contemplation on important subjects and withdrawal of sense organs is God.
- While practicing meditation make the mind and the sense organs introspect at the inner self and everyday before doing meditating develop a thought in mind that "I am not the physical body, I have nothing to do with wealth and any other worldly means of enjoyment; such as land, palatial residence, progeny, spouse etc. They do not represent my real being nor have they anything to do with me. I am independent of all tangible and intangible things of this phenomenal world. Even this physical body does not represent my real 'self' or the soul. I am independent of my body, sense organs and the subjects of their cognition. I am not the emotions that ripple the mind like passion, anger, attachment, pride or arrogance etc. I am the effulgent light which pervades the entire universe. I am bliss; I am a part of Brahma the creator. Like a water droplet rises from the sea water to the atmosphere and then again falls into the sea and gets mixed with the sea water, and so the water droplet does not leave the sea; similarly, I also do not want to leave God and want to be a part of Him and enjoy it. It is that God only who provides us with life, energy, momentum, glow, peace, joy and all the worldly means of enjoyment. God has given us birth, this life, energy, longevity, body, intellect, objects of pleasure, house, family, parents and everything else. Only God is giving me all joys. The peace and ultimate enjoyment from God is showering upon me from all directions. The mother Goddess and the father figure, the

saviors never leave me alone not even for a fraction of a second. The feeling that I am always with God and the God is always in me, will give us true joy. God is showering his never ending blessings on us. If still, we do not experience that joy given to us, then the fault is at our end.

- The *sādhaka* should always have a feeling of wisdom and asceticism. He should treat himself as an exhibitor, remain as a witness and perform all the pious activities, considering them as a service to God. Doing work without being proud of having done a duty and performing a duty without expecting any reward for it, is considered as *Ķriyāţmak Dhyāna*.
- One should realise that the worldly objects and pleasures derived from them are the cause of sufferings. So long as the mind remains attached to worldly and sensual pleasures, till then complete surrender to God will not take place and without this, success in meditation and achieving the final stage of *Yog Samādhi* is impossible.
- In this way every aspirant must devote at least one hour everyday in practice of *Jap*, *Dhyāna* etc. By doing so the aspirant may be successful in getting rid of all his sufferings and achieve realization of 'God' in the instant genesis. One should always remember that the ultimate goal of life is self realization and achieving the blessings of God, and all the remaining activities and targets are secondary. This is what the sages say about this in the *Upanișads:*

Ih çedvedidaţh saţyamaști na .
cedihāvediņmahatī vinaśtiḥ
Ḅhuteśu bhuteśu viçiņtya dhēraḥ .
Preţyaşmālọkādmŗitā bhavaņti

(Kenopaniśad 2.5)

This *manţra* means that only a human being who begins to involve himself in religious activities now and is keen to know about God, is successful.On the contrary, if a person is busy with worldly pleasures then he is thoroughly wasting his precious time and life. That is why *Yog* and *Dhyāna* have importance in our life. Keeping this in mind we should meditate everyday and aim towards self-realisation.

In the whole process of meditation there are certain disciplines that must be observed by every one who practices it.

Disciplines - Rules to be observed

- For the *sādhaka* of meditation, celibacy is absolutely essential. Even a family man can greatly benefit himself through this gradual process. For this he also needs to restrain himself from momentous materialistic joys. Without it, culmination of the final goal is impossible.
- Food should be simple, pure and nutritive. Otherwise also, for any human being, it is necessary to have the right kind of food, the right amount of sleep and controlled celibacy for a disease-free life. Hence, it is obvious, that a *sādhaka* of *Yog* shall have to follow the rules pertaining to food habits, sleep and celibacy.
- Without restraining from passions and without observing rules no person can become proficient in *Yog*. It is due to this reason that for *Kuṇḍalinī Jāgaran*, total cleansing and piercing of the *Çhakras* and attaining the state of *Samādhi*, passions are to be restrained and the rules must be observed compulsorily. Generally speaking, when you start practice of *Yog* on a daily basis, following the aforesaid methods, then restraining from passion and observing rules will become very easy as non-violence and truth are your natural and obvious qualities. You may be afraid of the feeling that you will not be able to observe rules and will not be able to become a full-fledged yogi, but do not worry as this is not the case. You just keep on following the aforesaid method for performing *Yog*, and your life will automatically adopt it. A lot of reverence, faith and belief will firm up in you for the rules like non-violence and truth that you will never ever have a desire to speak untruth. None of the feelings of violence with anyone will arouse. This is why, *Yog* is called the religion of our own body.

Precautions :

- The aforesaid yogic practices and observance of methods and procedures can be done by everyone enjoying normal health, but those, who are suffering from ailments like hypertension, heart diseases, asthma and other respiratory problems, should do yogic exercises slowly, carefully and gradually and none of the *Prāṇāyām* should be performed in haste. Doing *Prāṇāyām* in this way will rid the person of the diseases he was suffering from and he will progress further in *Yog*. Otherwise, by performing *Prāṇāyām* in haste the bloodpressure can rise and heart patients and the patients of asthma may face difficulties. One should be aware of the capability of his body and should never practice beyond such capacity.

- Before beginning the yogic exercise it is necessary to clear the bowels. Those suffering from constipation should take any mild laxative. Even otherwise, after practicing for a few days, diseases like constipation etc. get cured with no medication .
- By following the above rules; the *sādhaka* will have a good appetite. Hence, he should also take simple, delicious and nutritious food. This may include cow's milk, *ghēe*, seasonal fruits and almonds soaked in water etc. Even if a person is suffering from heart diseases, high cholesterol or high bloodpressure, he should consume *ghēe*, cow's milk and almonds soaked in water in small quantity.
- In summer season, the yogic exercises should be done for short durations only.
- If the *Kuṇḍalinī Jāgaran* occurs on some occasion, one should not believe that in future without any attempt to follow the prescribed disciplines and rules, one will be able to awaken this cosmic energy always. For this a healthy mind and a healthy body is a must. Cleanliness, purity, subtleness, purity in thoughts and continuous asceticism is to be maintained. In the absence of all these the process can come to a halt.
- The aspirant should always avoid vices like ostentation, empty show, pride etc. and he should remain calm, simple, casual, and down to earth. He should be moderate in speech. He should not aspire for appreciation, fame, publicity etc.

The symptoms and benefits of *Kuṇḍalinī Jāgaran*

It is not possible to describe in words the benefits that accrue from *Kuṇḍalinī Jāgaran*. It can, however, certainly be said that the condition is very pleasant and blissful. After achieving this end nothing more is left to be achieved. A feeling of total satisfaction, total peace and utmost pleasure is felt in the mind. By sitting next to such a person there is a feeling of peace in other persons too. If a person achieves *Kuṇḍalinī Jāgaran,* he can influence all those who come in his contact and enable them to shed their negative qualities, lead them to a virtuous path and enhance their faith in God. In addition to this, such a person has a divine glow, luster, sharpness and charm on his face. Grace in his body also begins to show. His face displays an expression of cheerfulness and equality. His sight also displays equality, compassion and divine love. His heart also becomes extensive, and there are expressions of divine generosity and kindness. His views become great and pious. In brief we can say that every aspect of his life is touched by purity, generosity and greatness.

The person doing all these *Yogīc* processes has spiritual benefits on one hand and on the other hand there is another benefit for him, which is, he never falls sick during his remaining lifetime and he gets rid of several diseases including cancer, heart diseases, diabetes, obesity, all ailments of the stomach, imbalances of *Vāta*, *Pitta* and *Kapha* etc. The person is completely free from all illnesses. That all diseases can be cured without the help of any medicine and one remains disease free, healthy, vigorous, strong minded and ascetic. Is this a small achievement for the selfish man of today's world ?

An Introduction to Divya Yog Mandir Trust, Kankhal

The headquarter of Divya Yog Mandir Trust is situated at Kripalu Bagh Ashram in Kankhal. This Ashram was established in 1932 by Swami Kripalu Devji Mahārāj who hailed from Mewar (Rajasthan) - the land of Maharanapratap. His name before becoming a *sanyasi* was Yati Kishore Chand. He played an active role in the freedom movement of India. At Haridwar, he harboured many revolutionaries and helped them to carry on their mission. Veni Prasad Jigyasu, a local freedom fighter was one of his close associates. Kripaluji was the man who collected around 3500 books and established the first public Library in Haridwar. He initiated dozens of schools for building the cultural base of the nation. Swami Shraddhanandji, founder of Gurūkul Kangri was a very good companion of Kripaluji. Later on, he came in contact of Balgaṅgādhar Tilak, Madan Mohan Malaviya, Motilal Nehru, Mahatma Gandhi, Chittaranjan Das, Ganesh Shankar Vidhyarthi, V.G. Patel, Hakim Ajmal Khan and many other nationalist leaders. Yati Kishore Chand joined the famous Bengali Revolutionary Group and took the responsibility of promoting and circulating 'Yugaṅtar' and 'Lokantar' - the mouthpiece of the revolutionaries. The British Government did not like these papers at all. The Government treated these papers like fire spitting dragons. Nobody was able to know about the place of publication of these papers. Yati Kishore Chandji dispatched these papers sometimes from Chandipahar in Haridwar and sometimes from Nildhara. Very often he dispatched these papers from his library at Paliwal Dharamshala. During this period, the Bengali Revolutionaries carried out the famous Hardings Bomb act in Delhi. Rasbehari Bose was the hero who was responsible for this act. Yati Kishore Chand was entrusted with the task to hide him in Haridwar. The British Government had already declared three lacs as a Prize on his head. Yati Kishore Chandji took him to his Ashram situated in a dense forest. Rashbehari Bose's friend Harish Babu came alongwith his three friends to see Yati Kishore Chand and informed him that the

British Government has smelt his presence in Haridwar. He may be hunted down anytime. Yati acted promptly. Rashbehari Bose boarded the Dehradun Express going to Banaras with a band of Patiyalvi passengers. In the wee hours of the next day, the police raided the ashram but by the time Mr. Bose was out of reach. Later Mr. Bose went to Japan. Then Yati Kishore Chand took *Sanyas*, and came to be known as Swami Kripalu Maharaj. He published a monthly magazine titled "*Vishwagyan*" to arouse the flame of independence among fellow Indians. Later on he switched to the yogic Sciences and Spiritualism and became a great yogi. He departed for his heavenly abode in the year 1968.

After Kripaluji's death, his disciples took the mission of their Gurū and began to manage the Ashram. Swami Shankardevji is the one of his chain of disciples who is the *Gurū* of Swami Ramdevji Maharaj. Divya Yog Mandir Trust was founded in the year 1995 by Shri Ramdevji with active assistance of Acharya Balkrishanji,Swami Muktanandji and others to carry on various selfless service projects in the service of mankind. His work has deeply affected the Indian society as a whole. They have promoted the confluence of *Veda*, *Yog* and *Āyurveda* far and wide. Billions of people are benefited with the yogic teachings of Swami Ramdevji. Every minute of his life is spent only in the service to humanity. Being a *sanyāsī* he is relentlessly seeking the path of the benevolence of the masses. He is simply devoted to this mammoth work. He believes that all that is happening and that is going to happen in future is because of the blessings of the Almighty God.

Service Organisations run by the Trust

In such a short period of even less than ten years the *Trust* has witnessed a phenomenal development in its various projects, from which, it seems nothing less than a Divine Miracle. The most ambitious project of Patanjali Yogpeeth has taken a multidimen-sional shape, looking at it people think that *Swami Ramdevji* is definitely blessed with some Divine Power. This miracle is the cumulative result of dedication towards the humble cause of serving the mankind, for which *Swamiji* is always inspired and prepared.The brief description of the different projects run by the Trust is as follows:-

Organising *Yog Sādhnā* and *Yog* Treatment Camps

The different *Yog Sādhnā* and *Yog* Treatment Camps organised in different parts of the country have foiled the misbelief that *Yog* is merely a physical exercise. Revered *Swamiji* has established *Yog* for spiritual development, physical fitness, mental, calmness, intellectual and all-round development and manifestation of human personality. In the yogic Camps the *Aṣṭāṅg Yog* emulated by Maharishi Patanjali is seriously dealt with. Apart from *Aṣṭāṅg Yog*, *Haṭh Yog*, Philosophies of the *Upanishad, Vedas, Çharak, Suśhrut* and many other subjects also are seriously dealt with in the camps. Arrangements are being made to give practical training for *'Yog'* and *Japa-Yog*, along with all the six folds of *HaṭhYog-Yog*, *Neti, Dhōuti, Basṭi, Ṭrāṭak, Nōuli* and *Kapalbhati.*

Braḥmakalpa Çhikiṭsālaya

Braḥmakalpa Çhikiṭsālaya treats its patients with *Yogic Śhaṭkaṛma* and *Paṇçhkaṛmā* (Massage, -Perspiration, Vomit, Purgative medicated enemas, Nasal administration of herbs) systems. Apart from that, herbal based medicines, proper and harmonious living, practicing *Ḅraḥmacharyā* and regulating the life activities are some of the tenets which are also attached with the treatment. Accupressure, *Yogasanas*, *Pranayam* and Naturopathy are taught at the centre either free or at nominal charges.

At *Braḥmakalp*, High Blood Pressure, Diabetes, Heart diseases, Asthma, Obesity, Acidity, Allergy, Ulcer, Cervical Spondolitis, Sciatica, Arthritis, Cancer (first and second stage) and many other chronic diseases are treated without surgery.

The *Çhikiṭsālaya* is being expanded to make it a residential *Chikiṭsālaya* so that many more patients can be accommodated and benefit out of it.

Swamiji firmly believes that we should prevent ourselves from falling ill. If unfortunately, we fall prey to illness we should prefer *'Yog'* and treat ourselves. If medicines are required, we should prefer *Āyuṛveda* because it is the most suitable system rooted to our environment, culture and nature and is hundred percent safe. Therefore, the medicines prepared in the pharmacy section are pure, effective and comparatively cheaper. Various preparations like *Bhāṣhyam, Pishti, Ras, Rasayan, Vati, Guggul, Churna, Awaleh, Sat, Kwath, Ghrit, Tel, Lauh Mandur, Parpati* and many more are available at *Braḥmakalp*. There is a huge requirement

Divya Pharmacy

of these medicines which we are unable to meet at present.

Very recently this pharmacy has been expanded so as to meet the requirement. The project for this has been completed.

Research Laboratory

Divya Yog Mandir Trust has a very sophisticated research laboratory where continuous research on different herbs is carried out. Its main objective is to rediscover rare medicinal herbs, preparation of *Āyurvedic* medicines as per the traditional methods, to keep pace with the latest develop-ments in the field of *Āyurvedic* research and publishing literature on *Āyurveda* in the greater interest of mankind. Our path breaking research of relocating the famous *Aṣṭavarga* herbs is praiseworthy. It has also prepared its own formu-lations, which have been successful and have earned praise all over. Our researchers have located these herbs at the very high altitude of the *Himalayas*. The Trust has published an exclusive book on *Aṣṭavarga* both in *English* and *Hindi*.

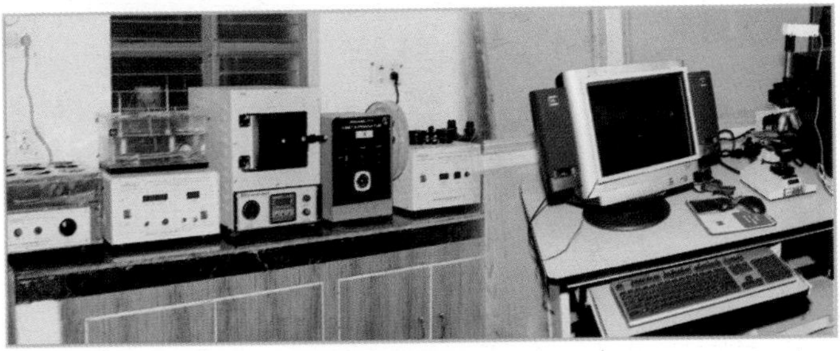

Research Laboratory

Herbarium

Herbal Garden

The Trust is striving for plantation, preservation and promotion of rare medicines in its herbarium. Owing to space constraints the project could not be given the desired shape. In the near future, the herbarium would be able to cater to the herbal requirements of the pharmacy and the general masses. Medicinal plants potted in earthen pots and seeds shall be available for sale.

Establishment of *Divya Goṣhālā*

Preservation of the Indian breed of the holy cow has been given utmost priority because various cow-related products are essential in treatment and formulation of medicines. There is a plan of preserving thousands of cows in the *Goṣhāla*. The cow dung will be used to make compost and fertilizer which will help cultivation of farm product at the Ashram, so that the produce is free from chemical fertilizers etc. Apart from this is a *Gobar* gas plant will also be installed to meet the energy

requirements of the Ashram. These Indian cows will be bred from the point of view of improving the breed of the cow, as also to give respect and recognition to it.

Vēdic Yagyaśhālā (*Agnihoṭra*)

Agnihoṭra in itself is a great science for purification of the environment, controlling drought and excess rainfall and treating certain diseases. *Agnihoṭra* can play a vital role in this. To perpetuate the

age long *ṛiṣhi* tradition of *Agnihoṭra*, one huge *Yagyaśhālā* in the *Pataṇjali Yogapeeth* complex has been built. There will be scientific research on the *Yagya* and *Yagya* related benefits.

Vēdic Gurūkula

A *Vēdic Gurukūla* at *Kishangarh Ghasera*, some 8 kms away from *Rewari* town in *Haryana*, is being run by the Trust, free of cost to disseminate standard teaching strictly on *Vēdic* pattern. Here both rich and poor students can obtain quality education without discrimination. The *Gurukūla* needs expansion so that greater number of students can be imparted education there.

Sādhna Ashram situated at *Gaṇgoṭrī*

At *Gaṇgoṭrī*, an *Ashram* has been established to conduct research on rare *Himalayan* herbs. The *Ashram* is yet to be expanded and given a new shape.

Establishment of *Pataṇjali Yogpēeth*

This Yogpeeth is a dream project of Divya Yog Mandir Trust which will spread over 1,000 acres of land. This Yogpeeth will play a vital role in spreading the message of *'Yog'* and *Āyuṛveda* among the masses. This will be able to

The main Gate of Patanjali

accommodate 6,000 to 10,000 patients per day and will consists of 500 beds, spacious halls, Pharmacy, Hospital, *Goṣhālā*, Herba-rium, Publication House, Library, Printing-Press, Community Kitchen for visitors, *'Yog'* Centre and other activities centres. The visitors to this Campus will avail pure food, which will be void of L.P.G., chemical fertilizer and insecticides. It will be developed as a cosmopolitan, self-reliant complex similar to the *Shantiniketan* of Late *Rabindranath Tagore*, and will also be a place of faith in the form of a renowned institute for public at large, which will bring Health, *'Yog'*, Mental Peace and Spiritual Development to crores of people. This ambitious project will cost around Rs. 100 crores, which will be generously offered by true *'Yog' Sādhaka*s and the well wishers of *'Yog'* and Spiritualism. *Swami Ramdevji* has vowed by Lord Shiva to complete this task with active co-operation of *'Yog'* lovers. By the grace of God which is being accomplished in time on a regular basis. This first phase of this project has been completed, and operation has commenced.

The amount of contribution that has been fixed by the Trust towards becoming a member of the Trust is as follows:-		
1.	**Founder Member**	**Rs. 5 Lacs**
2.	**Patron Member**	**Rs. 2. 51 Lacs**
3.	**Life Member**	**Rs.1 Lac**
4.	**Respected Member**	**Rs. 51 thousand**
5.	**Honoured Member**	**Rs. 21 thousand**
6.	**General Member**	**Rs. 11 thousand**

Publication of *Yog - Sandesh* (Monthly Magazine in Hindi)

On demand of thousands of *Sādhaka*s related to Divya Yog Mandir Trust, this magazine has been published in Hindi, English, Marathi, Bengali, Punjabi, Gujarati, Asamese, Nepali, Telugu, Kannada and Oriya editions under the expert guidance of noted editors since September, 2003. Every month thousands of new members are adopting this magazine, which proves its popularity amongst its readers. It has been decided that in the near future the views of sages on the subjects of *'Yog'*, *Āyuṛveda*, culture & rituals and spiritualism will be distributed among lacs of readers. Apart from this, poetry, articles of interest to public at large and the activities and future projects and the experiences and feelings of the readers shall also be included in the magazine. The popularity & fame earned by the Hindi Magazine in a short span of time, clearly shows that this is due to the popularity of *Swami Ramdevji Maharaj*.

Publications of the Trust

Glossary

Agni - It is Fire, one of the five elements. It is the biological fire that governs metabolism. It is similar in its function to *Pitta* and can be considered an integral part of the *Pitta* system in the body, functioning as a catalytic agent in digestion and metabolism. It is known as Fire, it is concerned with seeing, related to the eyes by the action of movement (walking).

Ajapā-Jap - It is the recitation of the *Manṭras* without the movement of lips i.e. it is silent recitation of *manṭra* done in the mind.

Ākāsha - It is known as Ether, one of the Five elements. It is concerned with sense of hearing, related to the ear, and is concerned with speech.

Āsanas - *Āsanas* are the postures, to be performed by the sadhaka as per the guidance of the teacher of the *Āsanas*. These postures depend on the disease which is to be cured.

Aṣṭāṅg Yog - Translated as Eight-fold *Yog*, it is a divine science discovered by the learned saints and seers of ancient India, brought into a disciplined manner, preserved and produced by Saint Patanjali in the form of eight yogic principles. *Yam* (Resistance to Passions), *Niyam* (Rules), *Āsana* (Postures), *Prāṇāyām* (Exercise of Breath), *Pratyaha*r (Resistance to Senses), *Dhāraṇā* (Concentration), *Dhyāna* (Meditation), and *Samādhi* (Union with the Infinite) are the Eight principles. A person practicing these principles is known to experience individual and social equality, physical health, intellectual awareness, mental peace and bliss of the soul

Āyuṛveda - It is a wholistic system of medicine that is indigenous to and widely practiced in India. The word *Āyuṛveda* is a Sanskrit term meaning "Science of life." *'Ayu'* means life and *'Veda'* is knowledge.

BahryaKuṃbhak - The stage of *Prāṇāyām* where the air is kept out i.e. not to inhale.

Bandhās - These are the lockings which are done by holding a particular organ or movement inside the body for a prescribed time. These enhance the effect of the activity for which they are prescribed.

Brahma - It means the Creator. Brahma is the God of creation.

Ḅraḥmaçāri - The person who follows the path of celibacy.

Çhaḳra - Energy centers in the body that are responsible for the different levels of consciousness; they correspond physiologically to the nerve plexus centers. They regulate the functioning of the vital organs of the physical body by providing the energy needed by them.

Çharak - A great *Ayurvēdic* physician who wrote one of the classic texts of *Āyuṛveda* : *Çharak Samhita*.

Çhitta - It is the mind, the faculty of reasoning & emotions. It has the nature of always being unstable, it can be controlled by practicing certain exercises.

Dhāraṇā - It is the state of steadiness of the mind. It is one of the principles of *Aṣṭāṇg Yog*.

Dhyāna - It is meditation or concentration of the mind over a thought or object. It improves mental well being of an individual who practices it. It is one of the principles of *Aṣṭāṇg Yog*

Doṣas - These are the Humors in the body. The three *Doṣas* are called *TriDosha*. They are due to three bodily organizations – *Vāta* (air) *Pitta* (fire) and *Kapha* (water) – which govern the psychosomatic activity of daily living.

Gāyatrī Manṭra - A *manṭra* from the Vedas, considered one of the greatest, and used extensively for the purpose of meditation or chanting

Ghēe - Purified butter made from cow's milk

Gurū - The teacher or the preceptor, here who initiates & guides one in the practice of *Yog* or attainment of *Mokṣa* or liberation.

Jīvan - It means life. It is there as long as the person is alive.

Kuṃbhak - The stage in *Prāṇāyām* where the air so inhaled is retained in the body for some time.

Kuṇḍalinī Jāgaran - The awakening of the divine coiled energy called *Kuṇḍalinī Śhakti* lying in the *Mūlādhāra Çhakra.*

Kuṇḍalinī Śhakti - It is the cosmic energy situated at the base *Çhakra* in the body. It is present there in coiled form like that of a serpent.

Mala - The three waste products of the body i.e. faeces, which is solid; urine and sweat, which are liquid.

Manṭra - Its singular form is *Manṭram*; it is a Sanskrit term denoting a word or group of words that carries certain phonetic vibrations and energy. Certain sacred Sanskrit words carry tremendous energy and chanting those words in a prescribed manner releases this energy.

Mūlādhāra- Çhakra - It is the *Çhakra* located at the base of the body.

Nāḍīs - These are the channels through which the energy flows in the body. They are *Prāṅic* currents of energy in the body.

Nāḍī Sōdhana Prāṇāyām - *The Prāṇāyām* that purifies the channels of energy flow.

Om - It is the first cosmic soundless sound.

Pañchakośas - The human soul (the animating force) is surrounded by five sheaths one above the other, and the outer sheaths penetrating the inner ones. These sheaths are called *Kośas*.

Pūrak - It is the stage in *Prāṇāyām* of inhalation of the air.

Prāṇa - It is vital energy (life-energy) which activates the body and mind. It is responsible for the higher cerebral functions, and the motor and sensory activities.

Prāṇāyām - It is the breathing exercise and is a yogic healing technique that can bring extraordinary balance in the consciousness. While practicing *Prāṇāyām* one experiences pure being and learns the true meaning of peace and love. It has many healing benefits and also affects creativity. It can bring joy and bliss into ones life.

Pṛithvi **-** It is known as Earth, one of the five elements. It is concerned with the sense of smell, related to nose by the action of excretion.

Puruśa **-** It is the male energy. It is formless, colorless and beyond attributes and takes no active part in manifestation of the Universe. This energy is choiceless, passive awareness.

Rajoguṇa **-** Derived from the word *Rajas*. It is the active vital life force in the body which moves both the organic and inorganic universes. It is the dynamic movement.

Rēchak **-** The process of exhalation of air out of the body is called *Rēchak.*

Sādhaka **-** The seeker of knowledge, wisdom. Here the person who practices *Yog*.

Samādhi **-** The merging of individual consciousness into the Cosmic Consciousness brings *Samādhi*, the state of highest equilibrium. In that state peace and joy will descend as a benediction. It is a state of equilibrium giving supreme joy and bliss. It is transcendental meditation, a principle of *Aṣṭāṇg Yog*.

Saṃkhyā **-** It is the philosophy of creation.

Sanyās **-** It is abandonment of worldly ties, asceticism.

Sanyāsī **-** A person who has abandoned worldly ties or has adopted asceticism. An ascetic.

Satoguna **-** Derived from the word *Satva*. It is the creative potential. It is stability.

Sātvika **-** It means simple, plain, without any show off in relation to life, or spicy with regard to food.

Shiva **-** A God of the Hindus, revered as the creator of th universe and an all powerful one.

***Shiva Saṇkalp* -** A vow taken while perfoming meditation or *Prāṇāyām*, the objective of such practise.

***Trīdośa* -** The three bodily organizations – *Vāta* (air) *Pitta* (fire) and *Kapha* (water) – which govern the psychosomatic activity of daily living.

***Triveṇī* -** Popularly known as the *Triveṇī Sangam,* it is the sacred place of confluence of the three rivers, *Gaṅgā, Yamunā* and *Sarasvatā* at Prayag in Allahabad India. Here it signifies the confluence of three *Nāḍī*s.

***Upaniṣads* -** The parts of the vedas which contain discourses on divine knowledge.

***Vāyu* -** It is known as Air, one of the five elements. It is concerned with the sense of touch, related to the skin by the action of holding it.

***Vedas* -** It means world's oldest extant literature, the oldest scriptures of Hinduism.

***Yog* -** *Yog* is the ancient life-disciplines that have been practiced in India for centuries. *Yog* is the science of union with the Divine, with Truth. Its practice helps the individual to achieve longevity, rejuvenation and self-realization.